ADVANCED VOCABULARY IN CONTEXT

DONALD WATSON

GEORGIAN PRESS

Georgian Press (Jersey) Limited
8 Duhamel Place
St Helier
Jersey JE1 3WF
Channel Islands

First published by Georgian Press (Jersey) Limited 1997

ISBN 1-873630-12-3 (without key)
ISBN 1-873630-13-1 (with key)

Produced by **AMR** Limited

Printed in Great Britain

Acknowledgements

The author and publishers are grateful to the following for permission to reproduce copyright articles:

The Daily Telegraph for 'Poor-spelling SCRABBLE inventor dies', 8.4.93, and *The Sunday Telegraph* for the extract from 'Sixth sense helps to watch your back', 14.4.96. Reproduced by permission of Ewan MacNaughton Associates, © Telegraph Group London, 1993/1996.

The Economist for the extracts from 'An elephantine problem', 30.3.96, 'Growing pains', 20.4.96 and 'What works?', 6.4.96. © The Economist, London, 1996.

The Guardian for the extracts from 'Airport lessons put flying fear to flight', 4.8.90 and 'Computer giant in a garage', 28.3.96, and for 'TB will kill 30m in next 10 years', 22.3.96 and 'Global warming disaster on way', 16.2.96.

The Independent for the extracts from 'How to be smarter with the same brain' by M O'Connor, 2.5.96, 'After the gloom, a lighter outlook' by A Brown, 4.96, the obituary of James Rouse by E Helmore, 12.4.96 and 'Lethal shockwave from an island in the sun' by P Henry, 24.6.96.

The Independent on Sunday for the extracts from 'It took 80 years to act' by G Lean, 7.4.96, 'A new view of home' by M Redfern, 21.4.96 and 'The greedy cities' by G Lean, 14.4.96.

The London Evening Standard for 'Stone Age hunters and the oldest wives' tale', 19.4.96. Reproduced by permission of Solo Syndications.

New Scientist for 'Someone to watch over me', 20.1.96.

TIME magazine for the extracts from 'Have Phone, Can Travel' 27.5.96 and 'Cashing in on Tomorrow', 15.7.96, and for 'Hazards Aloft', 22.2.93. © TIME Magazine.

The Times for 'Boy invested £100,000 during school breaks' by Craig Seton, 7.11.87. © Times Newspapers Limited, 1987.

We have unfortunately been unable to contact the copyright holders of 'The oldest masters of all' (*The Independent on Sunday*, 31.3.96) and 'Mapping your way out of mediocrity' (*The Daily Telegraph*, 14.6.95), and would welcome any information which would enable us to do so.

Cover design by George Mansolas.

CONTENTS

The Key begins on page 113 of the With Key edition.

INTRODUCTION

THE PURPOSE OF THIS BOOK

The purpose of **Advanced Vocabulary in Context** is to enable advanced-level students to practise vocabulary in natural contexts, to help develop an awareness and appreciation of collocation, and to prepare for certain gap-filling sections in examinations such as Cambridge CAE and CPE (Proficiency). It is suitable for use in the classroom, for homework, or (in the case of the With Key edition) for self-study.

HOW THE BOOK IS ORGANISED

There are 24 four-page units arranged thematically in four groups of six. They can be done in any order, although *within each group* the units are ordered approximately in terms of difficulty. After each group of units there are two Review pages to test how well some of the most useful phrases from those six units have been retained. The Key contains all the answers, plus the complete texts, not simply the answers to the gaps.

HOW EACH UNIT IS ORGANISED

Each unit is built around an extract or a complete article of up to 600 words from a quality newspaper or magazine (see Acknowledgements on page 3), in which approximately 40-50 words have been blanked out. These words are listed separately, and the text has to be completed by placing each word in the right position. This central exercise – ***Vocabulary in Context*** – is preceded by two preparatory sections – ***Vocabulary Check*** and ***Collocation*** – and followed by a final page of ***Further Practice***.

Vocabulary Check

In this first section of the unit, some of the words and expressions from the text that might be unfamiliar are defined and practised. Sometimes word elements are combined to form new words, which are also matched with definitions or practised in example sentences.

Collocation

In this group of exercises, some of the word combinations used in the text (noun + noun, adjective + noun, verb + noun, verb + adverb, etc.) are built up by matching words from lists, and these combinations are used in typical example sentences.

Vocabulary in Context

In this central exercise, the words listed before the text are used to fill the gaps in it. Nouns, adjectives, adverbs and sometimes participles are listed as they appear in the text, but verbs are listed in the infinitive and have to be put in the correct form according to the grammar of the sentence.

Further Practice

The final section of the unit contains various types of practice on vocabulary and idioms used in the text or related to it, including more collocations, word formation, figurative meanings, register and connotation. Occasionally there is an additional text for manipulation or gap-filling.

A NOTE ON COLLOCATION

Collocation is the placing together (*con* + *location* = 'with' + 'place') of words which are often associated with each other, so that they form common patterns or combinations. For example, *crimes* are not 'made' or 'done' but *committed;* we don't 'start' or 'begin' a *bank account*, but *open* it; in the middle of the day we don't have an 'interval', or a 'period' or a 'pause' for *lunch,* but a *lunch break*. (These three relatively easy collocations appear in Unit 1.) Using words together that do not commonly occur together, through ignorance of the normal collocation patterns, can make a person's English sound foreign. Using the normal collocations, on the other hand, makes their English sound natural and idiomatic.

HOW TO USE THE COLLOCATION EXERCISES

The best way for students to become familiar with the way words combine is to look first only at the lists of words and to try to match them in as many ways as possible. Only when they have made what they think are acceptable combinations should they try to use them in the sentences. There is only one way of using all the words once in the sentences, but by first manipulating and experimenting with many word combinations students gradually develop a greater awareness and appreciation of collocation.

OTHER WAYS TO USE THE GAP-FILLING EXERCISE

There are various ways in which the gap-filling exercise – ***Vocabulary in Context*** – can be made more testing or challenging. For example, students could complete the text

(a) without doing the first two sections (*Vocabulary Check* and *Collocation*) first as preparation

(b) without referring back to the wordlist, having read it through perhaps once or twice before starting the gap-filling exercise

(c) after hearing the teacher read out the complete text (from the Key), listening with their own books closed.

In the last two variations of this exercise other answers will often be possible, using words not included in the wordlist, so students may need to refer to the teacher to check their versions.

THE REVIEW PAGES

The Review pages are a way of checking that some of the most common word combinations (or collocations) from each unit have been learned. Each example has to be completed not with one missing word but with two words that are often used together in this way.

FINALLY ...

By the time students have done all the exercises in the book they will have increased enormously their ability to use the right words in the right combinations. And they will have enjoyed reading a wide variety of interesting and stimulating texts.

1 An enterprising schoolboy

VOCABULARY CHECK

Use these words to complete the explanations and definitions.

broker	invest	squad
deal	jargon	stock market
debtor	partner	watchdog
fraud	share	yuppie

1 When you ___________ money you put it to a particular use.

2 When someone commits ___________ they do something illegal or dishonest for financial gain.

3 A(n) ___________ is a person or organisation that tries to identify and prevent dishonest or undesirable practices.

4 A person who does financial business on another's behalf is called a(n) ___________.

5 If you have to use specialist terms in order to talk about a particular subject you have to learn the ___________.

6 A team of specially trained people with special duties is sometimes called a(n) ___________.

7 The capital stock of a company is divided into equal parts called ___________s.

8 A(n) ___________ is someone who owes money.

9 The ___________ is a place where parts of the ownership of companies are bought and sold.

10 A young person in a professional job with a high income is sometimes called a(n) ___________.

11 If a business is owned by two or more people who share the profits from it, they are known as ___________s.

12 If you ___________ on the stock exchange or stock market you buy stocks and shares.

Pairs

Find pairs of words with similar meanings. One of the words in the box on the right must be used twice.

tumble	fully-fledged
reveal	collapse
offence	claim
numerous	audacious
glean	

crime	show
daring	many
demand	mature
fall	pick up

COLLOCATION

Noun phrases

Combine nouns from each box to form suitable phrases. Then use the phrases to complete the sentences.

economics	share
fraud	Stock Exchange
lunch	telephone

break	order
jargon	ownership
lesson	squad

1 He missed his ____________ because he didn't go back to school after the ____________ .

2 She couldn't go to the shop in person so she placed a(n) ____________.

3 You have to learn all the ____________ if you want to understand the conversation of financial experts.

4 The ____________ is a section of the police that specialises in trying to catch people who commit crimes in their business or financial dealings.

5 Not many people invest money in companies on the stock market; ____________ is restricted to a relatively small proportion of the population.

Adjectives and nouns

Combine these adjectives and nouns to form suitable phrases. Then use the phrases to complete the sentences.

bad	latest	amount	loser
big	naughty	boy	losses
certain	senior	case	partner
estimated	tumbling	debts	prices
individual		jargon	

1 She's the ____________ in a firm of solicitors.

2 The Minister will answer questions on general principles but cannot comment on a(n) ____________.

3 It isn't skill; there's a(n) ____________ of luck in the game too.

4 ____________ are a big problem these days: many businesses have financial difficulties because clients don't pay their bills.

5 It's a buyer's market at the moment with these ____________.

6 Parents often don't understand what their teenage children are talking about because they are not familiar with the ____________.

7 He hates being called a(n) ____________ and says he's not a child any more.

8 They warned him that people don't automatically make a profit on the Stock Exchange. He turned out to be one of the ____________s with ____________ of over a million pounds.

Verb phrases

Which nouns can be used after which verbs? Make suitable phrases to complete the sentences, changing the form of the verb if necessary.

buy	meet	an account	money
cost	open	your case	an order
damage	place	your debts	shares

1 It ____________ to stay in hotels.

2 You can ____________ at the Stock Exchange.

3 You usually have to make a deposit when you ____________ at a bank.

4 You've seen all the goods we can supply. Would you like to ____________ now?

5 If you can't ____________ you might be declared bankrupt.

6 They say you should never admit fault in an accident as it might ____________ if it goes to court.

VOCABULARY IN CONTEXT

Complete the newspaper article, using one of these words for each space. You will need to change the form of some of the verbs. Use each word once only.

Nouns	*Adjectives*	*Verbs*	
behalf	audacious	buy	meet
debtors	aware	cost	open
economics	big	claim	reveal
firms	certain	comment	say
fraud	estimated	damage	slip
jargon	individual	deal	talk
offences	naughty	interview	tell
orders	senior		
ownership	tumbling		
shares	unnamed		
sides	worth		
watchdog	yuppie		

Boy invested £100,000 during school breaks

The Stock Market collapse claimed another victim yesterday when a __________ loser was __________ to be a boy, aged 15, who __________ home from school during lunch breaks to place telephone __________ for £100,000 __________ of shares with his brokers.

The schoolboy successfully passed himself off to brokers as a fully-fledged __________ businessman, aged 19, by using the latest Stock Exchange __________ gleaned from __________ lessons at his school in Derbyshire.

But the __________ dealings of the __________ schoolboy came uncomfortably to light when __________ Stock Exchange prices left the numerous brokers who bought __________ in companies on his __________ with __________ losses of £20,000 that he could not __________.

Mr Michael Somerset-Leek, __________ partner in Coni, Gilbert and Sankey, stockbrokers, one of the __________ used by the schoolboy, said yesterday: "Obviously he has been very __________. He __________ through our Wolverhampton office and has __________ us some money, but anything I say may __________ our case in __________ money from the lad."

Mr Somerset-Leek said that when a new customer __________ an account "there has to be a __________ amount of goodwill on both __________.

"It is just one of the problems of wider share __________," he added.

When the schoolboy started __________ shares his name was apparently cleared by the Stock Exchange Mutual Reference Society, an internal __________ that checks for bad __________.

Now the schoolboy is being __________ about "possible __________" by __________ squad detectives in Derbyshire. His headmaster said yesterday: "I am __________ of this boy's case, but it is not something I want to __________ about. All I can __________ is that he __________ me he went home at lunch-time and ordered shares there."

The Stock Exchange yesterday said it could not __________ on an __________ case.

FURTHER PRACTICE

Register

Read this conversation about the incident reported in the article. The phrases in italics are informal expressions, more typical of spoken language than of a written report.

A: Did you read about that *kid*[1] who went *bust*[2] on the Stock Exchange?
B: No. What happened?
A: Well, apparently this *lad*[3] of fifteen *skipped*[4] school and ... No, he didn't. He did it all in his lunch hour.
B: Did what? Get to the point.
A: Well, he phoned this firm of stockbrokers and *conned*[5] them into buying shares for him.
B: How did he *pull* that *off*[6]?
A: Well, I suppose he put on a *posh*[7] voice, you know, talking like a *grown-up*[8], and he'd done economics at school, so he knew all the *lingo*[9]. Anyway he *took* them *in*[10]. They must have thought he was *rolling in it*[11], judging by how much they invested for him.
B: Didn't they *check up on*[12] him first?
A: Well, his name wasn't on any blacklist, so they thought he was *a safe bet*[13]. Then the stock market *crashed*[14] and he lost *a fortune*[15].
B: That must have cost the brokers *a packet*[16].
A: Twenty thousand *quid*[17].
B: Good lord! However much did they invest for him?
A: A hundred *grand*[18], I think.
B: *More fool them*[19] for not making sure his story *checked out*[20].

Now match the expressions in italics with these explanations. Use three of them twice.

a adult
b bankrupt
c boy
d a good risk
e high-class
f jargon
g a lot of money
h pounds
i thousand pounds
j very wealthy
k investigate
l collapsed
m deceived
n missed
o succeed
p could be verified as true
q how stupid of them

Sentence adverbs

The adverbs *obviously* (line 11) and *apparently* (line 17) are called sentence adverbs because they modify a whole clause or sentence. We could replace these adverbs with phrases such as 'It is obvious to everyone that' and 'It appears that'. Match the following adverbs with phrases a – h, and then use the adverbs to complete the sentences.

sadly	**a**	if you want my honest opinion
foolishly	**b**	speaking for myself
undoubtedly	**c**	it is/was not a sensible thing to do
unexpectedly	**d**	it's a pity
naturally	**e**	I'm glad; it is/was fortunate
frankly	**f**	it is/was not anticipated
personally	**g**	there's no doubt about it
luckily	**h**	it's not surprising

1 ____________, I would never lend him anything.

2 ____________, I didn't take your advice. I wish I had.

3 ____________, his grandmother died just before he won the award.

4 ____________, she wanted to help. She's always been very kind to us.

5 He ____________ deserved to win. He definitely played better than the others.

6 ____________, we'd taken our umbrellas. As things turned out we needed them.

7 Quite ____________, he arrived home early one day and found them together.

8 ____________, I don't think he's got a chance of winning.

2 The man who invented Scrabble

VOCABULARY CHECK

Match these words with their definitions. Then use the words to complete the sentences.

craze	**a** a very keen interest in something
braille	**b** a brilliant idea
brainwave	**c** a form of printing that can be read by touch
copyright	**d** a popular fashion which does not last very long
royalty	**e** to grow and develop into its final, fully-developed form
mature	**f** payment made to writers, artists, inventors, etc. when copies of their work are sold
bug	**g** the legal right to produce copies of what someone has written, created or invented

1 The creators of the Superman character sold the ____________ for $200 when they were in their early twenties. They never received a single ____________ for all the films that were made.

2 He was bitten by the travel ____________ when he was a student and now spends two or three months abroad every year.

3 This game is the latest ____________ among teenagers.

4 This cheese isn't at its best yet. It needs a few more days to ____________.

5 When she started to go blind she decided to learn how to read ____________.

6 Suddenly he had a ____________. Why not sell everything and emigrate?

COLLOCATION

Noun phrases

Combine words from each box to form suitable phrases. Then use the phrases to complete the sentences.

board	agent
crucial	championship
department	decision
electronic	game
five-cent	page
front	royalty
home	sizes
marketing	store
varying	town
world	version

1 When she won the ____________ her name was on the ____________ of all the newspapers.

2 He went to a ____________ to buy a new ____________of his favourite ____________ – Scrabble.

3 He was only sixteen when he made the ____________ to leave his ____________ for good.

4 At first he received only a ____________ on each book sold, but his new ____________ negotiated much better terms.

5 These tee-shirts are made in ____________ to suit children and adults.

Verb phrases

Which of the nouns can be used after which verbs? Make suitable phrases to complete the sentences.

catch	the game
earn	on an idea
hit	with someone
master	a new name
take	royalties
team up	5 years
think up	no signs of
score	the bug
show	points

1 They never thought it would ____________ to make the company profitable.

2 He stopped writing twenty years ago, but he continues to ____________ from his early novels.

3 In the game of Scrabble you ____________ by using the letters you've been given to make words. It might look difficult at first, but you'll soon ____________.

4 He had never been very successful going into business alone. Then he ____________: he decided to ____________ and start a partnership.

5 They had to ____________ for it so that people would know it was a new product.

6 I never used to play cards, but once you ____________ it's not easy to stop, and now I play two or three times a week.

7 Aren't plants fascinating? They ____________ life for months and then they suddenly shoot up and burst into flower.

Common expressions

Combine words from these lists to form common phrases.

long	money
right	points
according to	experts
desperate for	the alphabet
the number of	first time
each letter of	sales
at the peak of	dead

VOCABULARY IN CONTEXT

Complete the newspaper article, using one of these words or phrases for each space. You will need to change the form of some of the verbs. Do not use any word or phrase more than once.

Nouns		*Adjectives, Adverbs and Participles*		*Verbs*	
alphabet	liking	available	national	call	interest
bestseller	peak	conventional	other	confess	master
bug	royalty	crucial	scored	dry up	pass
championship	sales	desperate	single	examine	take
department	signs	enough	sold	expire	team up
experts	use	first	varying	hit on	think up
home	version	long	wonderful	include	

Poor-spelling SCRABBLE inventor dies

The man who invented the word game Scrabble because he was __________ for money during the Great Depression has died, aged 93.

By the time Alfred Mosher Butts died in hospital in his __________ town of Rhinebeck, New York, __________ of the game had __________ 100 million and it had its own world __________. But the 1931 brainwave __________ 20 years to mature after Butts began by making the game in his garage and selling it to neighbours and anyone he could __________ .

Scrabble showed no __________ of becoming a bestseller until the owner of Macy's __________ store in New York caught the __________ while on holiday in 1952. Within a year it was a __________ craze.

However, Butts always said that Scrabble had never made him rich. By the time it had become a world __________, he earned only a five-cent __________ on each set __________, a deal which gave him about $50,000 a year at the __________ of sales in the fifties and sixties. His copyright __________ in 1974, and the income __________. He lived comfortably __________, however, from his work as an architect.

Butts first __________ his game Criss-Cross, and then Lexico. It became Scrabble in 1948, when Mr Butts __________ with a marketing agent, James Brunot. But who __________ the familiar name is lost to history; Brunot is __________ dead, and Butts recently said he could not remember who had __________ Scrabble.

Butts never __________ the game which combined his __________ for jigsaws and crosswords with his professional sense of pattern and space.

"When I played him, he __________ that he was not a very good speller, and I beat him," said Mr John Williams, president of the National Scrabble Association. "He was a __________ man, really a classic American genius."

Butts, according to __________, was most remarkable for getting the game right __________ time. The __________ decisions on the number of each letter of the __________ in each set and the number of points __________ when they are used to make words have never been changed, except to conform with the frequency of __________ in languages __________ than English.

Butts decided on the value of the letters by __________ the number of times they were used on a __________ front page of *The New York Times*.

The game is now __________ in __________ sizes and comes either as a __________ board game or in an electronic __________. Translations __________ French, Spanish, Hebrew and Russian, and there is a Braille version.

FURTHER PRACTICE

Vocabulary

Use these four words from the unit to complete the sentences. Compared with the way they are used in the article, they may have different meanings. Change the verb forms if necessary.

bug genius master mature

1 A __________ student is one who is older than most students, usually over twenty-five.

2 Several people are off work at the moment. There seems to be a __________ going round.

3 She had never been involved in marketing before, but she soon __________ the art of persuading people they needed what she was selling.

4 Everyone thinks of Sherlock Holmes as a brilliant detective with a ___________ for making deductions, but he was also a ___________ of disguise.
5 Be careful what you say. I think this room is ___________.

Expressions with *idea*

Complete each sentence with one of these words. Then continue each one by adding a sentence from the list below.

bright	faintest	good	hit	odd	put	toy	very	whole

1 I don't know what ___________ that idea into his head. ...
2 I've a pretty ___________ idea why they didn't come. ...
3 He's one of those people who are full of ___________ ideas. ...
4 I'm ___________ing with the idea of getting a new car. ...
5 He's got some very ___________ ideas about life. ...
6 I'm sorry, I haven't the ___________ idea. ...
7 He ___________ on a brilliant idea. ...
8 The ___________ idea of eating meat is repugnant to some people. ...
9 The ___________ idea of a charity is not to make a profit for the people who work in it, but to help other people. ...

a I simply don't know.
b That's what it's for.
c It probably won't happen though.
d They just can't countenance it.
e Unfortunately they hardly ever come to anything.
f I'm sure he didn't think of it himself.
g I can't be sure, but I have my suspicions.
h It was quite unexpected – pure inspiration.
i I can't begin to understand how his mind works.

Collocation and idiom

Combine these words or word endings with *rich* or *poor* to make common phrases. Then use the phrases to complete the sentences. What is the opposite or *rich* or *poor* in each case?

pay	food	health	at	-es	vocabulary
soil	quality	colours	in	-ly	-ly deserved

1 She's good at crosswords and has a very ___________.
2 Einstein was a genius, but he was ___________ maths at school.
3 The honours she received before her death were ___________.
4 He was in ___________ for the last five years of his life.
5 He painted in very ___________.
6 The ___________ of the Nile Valley made farming very successful in ancient Egypt.
7 They don't eat very much but their diet is ___________ vitamins.
8 This material isn't good enough for a suit. It's very ___________.
9 Her rise to fame was a classic rags to ___________ story.
10 How can people manage on such ___________?
11 You'll get indigestion if you eat such ___________.
12 I'm feeling a bit ___________. I think I'll lie down.

3 Computer giant and business genius

VOCABULARY CHECK

Match each word on the left with a word or phrase of similar or opposite meaning. Then use some of the words on the left to complete the sentences.

site	craze
mania	plate
plush	origins
scorn	luxurious
plaque	well maintained
shabby	order according to rank
tinker	university qualification
burgeon	develop rapidly
austere	play about
genesis	opulent
hierarchy	admire
degree	place

1 He used to spend hours ____________ing with old radios.

2 Bricks were stolen from the building ____________ at night.

3 The country owes its sudden economic success to its ____________ing oil industry.

4 She used to be very rich and had a very ____________ flat, but when religious ____________ swept the country she gave a lot of money away, saying she ____________ed wealth, and she started to live a very ____________ life.

COLLOCATION

Adjectives and nouns

Combine these adjectives and nouns to form suitable phrases. Then use the phrases to complete the sentences.

bronze	personal
classical	senior
informal	strict
new	

executive	music
fortune	plaque
hierarchy	style
invention	

1 Do you like listening to ____________?

2 There is a(n) ____________ on the house where Mozart stayed when he was in London.

3 The room is impressive, but I prefer a more ____________ of furnishing.

4 There is a very ____________in the company from the Chairman down to the junior clerks.

5 He worked as a(n) ____________for twenty years but made most of his ____________ from a(n) ____________ he came up with during his retirement.

Electronic or electronics?

Which word, *electronic* or *electronics*, can be used before these nouns?

an ____________ calculator

an ____________ company

an ____________ engineer

____________ equipment

____________ instruments

the ____________ industry

Noun phrases

Combine words from each box to form suitable phrases. In one case the two words join together to form a single word.

birth	board
drawing	corridors
industrial	floor
leafy	house
office	office
opulent	place
plush	site
shop	street

Verb phrases

Which of the phrases can be used after which verbs? Use some of these expressions to complete the sentences.

go	a site
own	a coin
lose	public
make	your job
take	a living
form	a building
toss	to the view
put up	a partnership
subscribe	advantage

1 When people can't decide whether or not to do something they sometimes ____________.

2 If you don't want to go into business alone we could always ____________.

3 It's not easy to ____________ these days if you have no qualifications.

4 The company was now worth several million pounds and they decided it was time for it to ____________.

5 If they're selling two for the price of one, she'll buy several, whether she needs them or not. She simply has to ____________ of an offer whenever she sees one.

6 Many people ____________ that everyone is basically dishonest.

VOCABULARY IN CONTEXT

Complete the newspaper article, using one of these words or phrases for each space. You will need to change the form of some of the verbs. Use each word or phrase once only.

Nouns		*Adjectives and Adverbs*		*Participles*	*Verbs*	
board	floor	annually	leading	born	form	split up
capital	hierarchy	austerely	leafy	met	go	study
computer	invention	current	personal	put up	make	take
corridors	plaque	electronic	plush	regarded	obtain	tinker
degree	profit	eventually	popular		offer	toss
equipment	site	informal	shabby		recall	
executives	style					
field	wishes					

Computer giant in a garage

The monument to David Packard, the electronics engineer, is a bronze __________ on the lawn of a pleasant but not opulent house in a __________ street in Palo Alto, California. The house was not his birthplace, but its small and __________ wooden garage is regarded as the genesis of Silicon Valley and the computer industry.

5 It was here, in the 12-by-18ft building __________ in 1905, that Packard and his friend Bill Hewlett began in the autumn of 1938 to __________ with their new __________, an electronic audio oscillator that Walt Disney later used to test sound __________ for his classical music cartoon, Fantasia. So powerful was the legend of Hewlett-Packard's origins that today in the computer industry a failure is __________ not with "back to the drawing __________" but "back to the garage".

10 Packard, co-founder of the huge Hewlett-Packard electronics company, also invented a management __________ known as the "HP Way" that is still practised. It is __________ but efficient, and includes such concepts as "management by walking around", in which executives roam the shop __________ and office __________ meeting employees and seeking their ideas.

Packard was __________ the son of a successful lawyer and high-school teacher in the town of Pueblo, 15 Colorado, and despite the family's __________ for a law career, he __________ a master's __________ in electrical engineering at Stanford. He __________ under Professor Frederick Terman, who was concerned that so many of his brightest graduates went "back east" to __________ their living. The professor, now __________ as the father of the US electronics industry, wanted them to __________ their own companies on an industrial __________ the university owned. Packard and his fellow student Hewlett were among the 20 first to __________ advantage of the offer.

They formed their partnership on New Year's Day 1939 with just $538 in __________, and __________ a coin to decide in what order to put their names. "We weren't interested in making money," Packard __________ later, "but if you couldn't get a job, you made one for yourself. Our first several years we made only 25 cents an hour."

25 However, in the first year they had a __________ of $1,539 on sales of "inventions to order" of $5,369. Their company became a __________ supplier of __________ instruments and equipment that __________ led the partners into the burgeoning __________ of computers. They built their first model, the HP-2116a, in 1966, but made more money on the __________ electronic calculator they introduced in the early 1970s.

Today Hewlett-Packard is the second largest __________ company in the United States, with sales of 30 $31.5 billion __________ and 100,000 employees. Forbes magazine estimated Packard's __________ fortune at $3.7 billion, but he lived __________ and did not subscribe to the __________ "downsizing" mania in which hundreds of thousands of Americans from lathe operators to senior __________ have lost their jobs.

Packard wrote down his management beliefs when the company __________ public in 1957. It scorns a strict __________ but encourages individual creativity while urging a "company culture" of respect and trust. 35 Packard believed in dispersing power and would __________ divisions after they reached 1,500 employees. Executives at HP had no limousines or private dining-rooms, and Packard did away with __________ offices, installing cubicles without doors instead, while encouraging engineers to leave their work out so others could come by and tinker or __________ ideas.

FURTHER PRACTICE

Inventor vocabulary

There are many words for people who make something or do something for the first time. Use these words to complete the sentences. You will need to use two of them twice.

architect	discoverer	inventor
author	father	originator
creator	founder	pioneer
designer	instigator	

1 He made his name as a fashion ____________.

2 Marie Curie is famous as the ____________ of radium.

3 Christopher Wren was the ____________ of St Paul's Cathedral in London.

4 Dr Christian Barnard, the South African heart surgeon, was a ____________ in the field of transplant surgery.

5 He was the ____________ of his country's independence so it was natural that he should become its first President.

6 Walt Disney was the ____________ of the world-famous cartoon character, Mickey Mouse.

7 She collects first editions, signed by the ____________.

8 He left all his money to the hospital of which he was the ____________.

9 He was regarded as the ____________ of the revolt, even though he did not actually take part in it.

10 No one knows who the ____________ of the idea was.

11 I have no sympathy for him. He was the ____________ of his own downfall.

12 Lazlo Biro, a Hungarian by birth, was the ____________ of the ballpoint pen.

13 The Greek physician Hippocrates is regarded as the ____________ of medicine.

More collocations and vocabulary

Here are some phrases from the article. Change each one to a phrase of opposite meaning, by changing the words in *italics*. Use the new words or phrases to complete the sentences.

senior executive	*informal* style	*strict* hierarchy
form a partnership	*plush* offices	*industrial site*
opulent house	*subscribe to the same* view	*put up* a building

1 After working together for twenty-three years they finally decided to ____________ .

2 He didn't like the ____________ of his father and grandfather and adopted a relatively ____________ in the management of the family business.

3 Clerks used to work in very ____________ in those days.

4 They ____________ those ____________ a long time ago.

5 It makes no difference what view I subscribe to, she always ____________.

6 There are very few businesses here. It's mainly a(n) ____________ .

7 It was not the sort of house I would care to live in. In fact it was a(n) ____________.

8 She's just got a job as a(n) ____________ in a famous advertising agency.

How to develop genius

VOCABULARY CHECK

Find words with similar meanings in this list. There are seven pairs and two groups of three. Then use one of each pair or group to complete the sentences.

angst	consider	link	stress
anguish	encourage	period	tension
anxiety	follow	ponder	ties
bout	foster	pursue	trigger
connection	frailty	spark	weakness

1 How can we ____________ unselfish behaviour in young children?

2 Her childhood was marred by physical ____________ and she suffered long ____________s of illness.

3 Twentieth-century literature seems to have been characterised by profound feelings of existential ____________.

4 It is generally thought that ____________ makes one more susceptible to illness.

5 She's lecturing on the ____________ between the emotions and physical illness.

6 What makes some people decide to ____________ a life of crime?

7 The chess player spent ten minutes ____________ing his next move.

8 The new legislation ____________ed off mass demonstrations all over the country.

COLLOCATION

Adjectives and nouns

Combine these adjectives and nouns to form suitable phrases. Then use some of the phrases to complete the sentences.

final	physical
mental	creative
general	emotional
budding	outstanding
inner	statistical

arts	factors
tension	frailty
genius	analysis
rigour	population
illness	individuals

1 Deep breathing and relaxation exercises can help considerably in relieving ____________.

2 His childhood was spoilt because he spent so much time confined to his bedroom on account of his ____________.

3 No one was surprised when he went mad. After all there was a history of ____________ in the family.

4 Every mother thinks her first child is a ____________, but the number of ____________ in the ____________ is extremely small.

5 Is it really more satisfying to have a job in the ____________?

6 In the ____________ there are nearly always ____________ in the progress of any physical illness.

Noun phrases

Join words from each box by adding **of** to form suitable phrases. Use each word once only.

a bout	life
a blend	illness
a period	the ladder
a feeling	a profession
a variety	inferiority
a member	chemicals
the top	factors

Common phrases

Combine words from each box to make common phrases. Then use the phrases to complete the sentences. Use each word or phrase once only.

sit	contrary	from	to genius
clues	searching	the gap	of success
bridge	the secret	for clues	the findings
outline	as distinct	damaged	on the throne
emotionally	permanently	draining	to expectations

1 The police are still ___________.

2 How long did King Henry VIII ___________?

3 ___________ everyone enjoyed the party enormously.

4 She always said that ___________ and a long life was her habit of getting up early.

5 This book appeals to all ages. It is truly amazing how the writer manages to ___________ between the generations.

6 In his lecture he tried to ___________ of his research.

7 He insists on being called a personal assistant ___________ a secretary.

8 Apparently one of the ___________ is an unhappy childhood.

9 Working with the mentally ill can be ___________ but very satisfying.

10 Her father was ___________ by his experiences as a prisoner of war.

VOCABULARY IN CONTEXT

Complete the newspaper article, using one of these words for each space. You will need to change the form of some of the verbs. Use each word once only.

Nouns		*Adjectives, Adverbs and Participles*		*Verbs*
angst	link	budding	final	bridge
blend	loss	burdened	general	generate
bout	periods	contrary	ill	pursue
career	professions	creative	inner	rely
clues	rigour	crucial	instead	speculate
findings	sample	damaged	outstanding	subdivide
frailty	study	distinct	physical	
illness	variety	emotional	triggered	
leaders		emotionally	unlike	
		extremely		

Mapping your way out of mediocrity

For thousands of years, philosophers have pondered the ties between madness and creativity. Now this __________ has been examined with statistical __________ by Professor Arnold Ludwig of Kentucky University, who outlines his __________ in a new book.

__________ of leafing through medical notes searching for __________ to genius, Prof Ludwig __________ on biographies of 20th-century people reviewed in *The New York Times* from 1960 to 1990. In this way he gathered the names of 1004 poets, journalists, artists and business __________. He analysed the extent of mental __________ in each field, examined other __________ factors fostering greatness, then created a so-called template for success.

Prof Ludwig believes genius requires a precise __________ of brain chemicals (inherited) and environmental cues. Not surprisingly, he finds that "members of the artistic __________ or __________ arts suffer more types of mental difficulties and do so over longer __________ of their lives than members of other professions."

Prof Ludwig finds that 24 per cent of his sample had suffered the death of a parent before the age of 14. A previous __________ of 24 British prime ministers found that 63 per cent had suffered the __________ of a parent by the age of 15. The rate in the __________ population is 17 per cent.

"__________ to conventional expectations, not all people are permanently devastated or __________ by such a loss," Prof Ludwig writes.

Some 10 per cent of his __________ suffer genetic disability and another 10 per cent have suffered illness for at least six months during their youth. Prof Ludwig __________ that physical __________, like the death of a parent, sparks an inner __________, a feeling of inferiority, that drives children to excel.

The __________ clues to genius, the heart of Prof Ludwig's argument, are revealed in his __________ analysis, in which he __________ his sample to distinguish thinkers such as Albert Einstein or even Agatha Christie from élite such as kings. ("All they did was sit on the throne," Prof Ludwig says.)

__________ individuals tend to be born with talent, have creative parents, a mentally __________ mother, a tense household and a __________ of __________ illness. Above all else, Prof Ludwig highlights "psychological unease", as __________ from mental illness.

"This is __________ important because __________ past studies that have talked about mental illness, I talk about the sense of unease that __________ the gap between those who are motivated and driven and those who are normal psychologically but who have the capacity to __________ inner tension," Prof Ludwig says. This inner tension – whether __________ by a psychiatric illness or by the death of a loved one – encourages the __________ genius to bury himself in his work, sometimes at the expense of his happiness. Prof Ludwig believes true psychological unease is the result of a __________ of factors.

Now that we all have the secret of success, the real question is whether we want to __________ it. Do we want to endure chronic __________ tension to reach the top of the __________ ladder? Do we want to bring up children who are __________ by mental anguish? Not even the best psychiatrist can predict the path best for you, the merry stroll of mediocrity or the __________ draining ascent of success. And that, says Prof Ludwig, is why he called his book *The Price of Greatness*.

FURTHER PRACTICE

Negative prefixes

Notice that *unease* (lines 26 and 28) is not the same as *disease*: different negative prefixes are sometimes used with the same root for different meanings, or even for different parts of speech.

Use the appropriate prefix with these words to complete the sentences.

Prefixes		Words			
ab-	**in-**	ability	comfort	distinct	motivated
dis-	**un-**	able	conventional	easy	normal
im-		burdened	connected	inherited	

1. I can't see it clearly. It's very ____________.
2. He ____________ his daughter after she married against his wishes.
3. He's rather ____________; some would say eccentric.
4. No one behaves like that. It's ____________.
5. I had a(n) ____________ feeling that something terrible was going to happen.
6. She felt no pain or ____________ at all.
7. I'm sorry. I'm ____________ to help.
8. They ____________ him because he hadn't paid his electricity bill.
9. It's hard work teaching these students. They're so ____________.
10. He felt much better having ____________ himself, talking to the psychiatrist.
11. She can't use her left hand. She's had the ____________ ever since the accident.
12. The Minister insisted that the increase in crime was totally ____________ with the rise in unemployment.

Misleading 'negatives'

Not all words beginning with apparently negative prefixes such as *un-* or *in-* are actual opposites. In some cases the positive form no longer exists. Sometimes *in-* is a prefix with a different meaning.

Use the appropriate prefix to form words to complete the sentences.

Prefixes	Words			
dis-	-corrigible	-ept	-flammatory	-may
in-	-couth	-famous	-gainly	-nocuous
un-	-delible	-flammable	-kempt	-sidious

1. He was drinking and swearing all night. His behaviour was generally most ____________.
2. You can't wash this stain out. It's ____________ ink.
3. His ____________ attempts to compliment her merely made matters worse.
4. I'm not surprised they started fighting, after those ____________ remarks.
5. She's a(n) ____________ liar, but people just can't help liking her.
6. He was one of the most ____________ murderers in legal history.
7. He may look dangerous, but he's quite ____________ really.
8. She was filled with ____________ when she saw how much work she had to do.
9. Don't smoke near that tank. It's ____________.
10. Multiple sclerosis is a(n) ____________ disease that attacks the central nervous system.
11. He's very tall and has a peculiar ____________ walk.
12. I'm not surprised he didn't get the job, looking as ____________ as that.

5 The oldest creations of the human mind

VOCABULARY CHECK

Choose the correct definition of these words and expressions.

1 A *draught* is a) a period when there is little or no rain b) a current of air.
2 *Snaps* are a) the photographs we take when we are on holiday
b) small pieces that are cut off something bigger.
3 If you are *oblivious* you are a) unconcerned about something
b) not aware of something.
4 If you are *baffled* you are a) puzzled b) fascinated.
5 If something is *unprecedented* a) there has been nothing like it before
b) it has not been predicted.
6 If things are *in turmoil* they are a) in confusion and uncertainty
b) lost or difficult to find.
7 A *canyon* is a) a cliff b) a valley with steep sides.
8 *Rubble* is a) the noise made by a crowd of people
b) what is left when a building falls down.
9 If something is *controversial* a) people disagree about it.
b) it is impossible to disprove.
10 A *ritual* is a) a disorderly, sometimes violent, protest
b) a series of actions performed regularly, often as part of a ceremony.
11 A *masterpiece* is a) a great work of art
b) a person who is obsessed by power.
12 If something is *stunning* it is a) very beautiful b) very painful.
13 *Rival* means a) competing b) increasing.

COLLOCATION

Adjectives and nouns

Combine words from each box to form suitable phrases. Then use some of the phrases to complete the sentences.

academic	general	cave	prospects
burning	historical	circles	public
clear	research	find	purposes
future	vast	picture	torch

1 She wanted to know what his ____________ were before she married him.

2 She is against the use of animals for ____________.

3 It's a fascinating subject but this book is too specialised for the ____________.

4 He wasn't exactly famous, but he was well-known in ____________.

5 Many ____________s were discovered in the ____________ where early humans had lived and they gave a ____________ of what life in the Stone Age was like.

Noun phrases

Join words from these boxes with **of** or **to** to form suitable phrases. Then use the nouns on the right to complete the sentences.

areas	the find	the century	*Homo sapiens*
a clue	a network	galleries	the mystery
the emergence	a pile	the globe	stones

1 The catacombs were a network of underground ___________. The entrance was marked by a pile of ___________.

2 This discovery is the find of ___________ and tells us a great deal about the emergence of ___________.

3 It provides a clue to the ___________of how humans spread to all areas of the ___________.

More noun phrases

Join words from these lists with **of** to form phrases which complete the sentences.

a draught	**of**	artistic	ability
the evolution		human	air
the greatest		man's	colonists
groups		scientific	mind
the level		warm	mysteries

1 He felt ___________ coming from the kitchen.

2 ___________ migrated from Africa and settled in Asia and Europe.

3 ___________ achieved by Stone Age people is truly remarkable.

4 ___________ is one of ___________.

Adverbs with adjectives and participles

Combine these adverbs and adjectives and match each phrase with its definition.

largely	clear	**a** coming as a complete surprise
previously	dispersed	**b** scattered about
roughly	oblivious	**c** very similar
unprecedentedly	the same	**d** almost completely unaware
widely	unsuspected	**e** easier to understand than ever before

Re-ordering

Re-order these words to form acceptable phrases.

1 the paintings world's known oldest

2 the explanations main three rival

3 a(n) event global unsuspected environmental

4 the step spectacular intellectual most

VOCABULARY IN CONTEXT

Complete the newspaper article, using one of these words for each space. You will need to change the form of some of the verbs. Use each word once only.

Nouns	*Adjectives*	*Participles*	*Adverbs*	*Verbs*
circles	artistic	baffled	controversially	disperse
clues	clear	burning	partly	engage
draught	future	known	previously	evolve
evidence	general	lived	roughly	explain
evolution	inexplicable	sealed	simply	hope
find	oblivious	thrown	simultaneously	illuminate
groups	oldest	undetected	suddenly	mention
implications	outside	verified	widely	represent
network	rival			roam
opportunity	separate			suggest
pile	significant			trigger
purposes	vast			

The oldest masters of all

One 18 December 1994, three French cavers were exploring a canyon in southern France when they felt a __________ of warm air coming from a __________ of stones. They removed the rubble, and uncovered a __________ cave that had been __________ off from the __________ world for hundreds of centuries. Inside, they found themselves face to face with more than 200 cave paintings of animals that once __________ Europe: rhinos, lions, bears and bison – stunning portraits now __________ as the world's __________ known paintings.

Academic __________ have been __________ into turmoil by the discovery of what is now __________ (after one of the cavers who found it) as the Chauvet cave. Most of the rest of the world remains largely __________ to the excitement. Apart from a few initial snaps in the press, there has been little __________ for the __________ public to admire the paintings, the cave itself having been sealed for research __________.

Preliminary research __________ that the 35,000-year-old drawings were __________ religious in nature. The cave, in the Ardèche, in south-east France, was never __________ in by humans. Rather, it was a pitch-dark hidden __________ of galleries, some of them 30m high and 70m long; the Stone Age artists would have required __________ torches to __________ it.

The drawings show a level of __________ ability __________ unsuspected for the period. Each masterpiece features perspective, shadow – even movement. But the Chauvet cave is far more than __________ the art __________ of the decade. It may also offer __________ to one of the greatest of all scientific mysteries: the __________ of man's creative mind.

Homo sapiens evolved in Africa some 150,000 years ago, and __________ around the world about 100,000 years ago. However, there is no __________ of art having existed until around 40,000 years ago. Then, over the following 12,000 years, in Australia, Europe and southern Africa, there seems to have been an as yet __________ intellectual revolution in which art was produced. Scientists have long been __________ as to how creative thought developed almost __________ in three such __________ areas of the globe. Clues in the Chauvet cave – footprints, handprints, bones – may, by offering an unprecedentedly __________ picture of prehistoric ritual, help to __________ how and why humanity in this period __________ became able to __________ in symbolic thought.

There are three main __________ explanations. First, there could have been an as yet __________ global environmental event which __________ the rapid simultaneous development of creative thought. Second, it could be that, after spreading out from Africa, the __________ dispersed __________ of human colonists each progressed culturally at __________ the same speed, despite different environments. Or, most __________ of all, it could be that the human brain continued to __________ – rapidly, in evolutionary terms – *after* the emergence of *Homo sapiens*.

If this last theory is correct, the __________ for evolutionary and psychological thinking, not to __________ humanity's __________ prospects, might be considerable. The paintings are spectacular – but the cave's interest is that, in the words of Jean Clottes, senior archaeologist at the site, "Our research will help us to understand what the Stone Age artists were *doing* in the cave." Let us __________ that it does: for the revolution in human thought which the paintings __________ was perhaps the most __________ intellectual step ever taken by mankind.

FURTHER PRACTICE

Time expressions

*... hundreds of **centuries*** (line 3), *... the art find of the **decade*** (line 18).

Complete the sentences with these words. Some are used more than once.

age	era	history	period
century	fraction	hour	prehistory
decade	historic	light year	second
eon	historical	millennia	turn

1 It was a(n)____________ moment when the President opened the new bridge linking the two countries. It really made history and marked the beginning of a new ____________ .

2 He was born around the ____________ of the ____________ and fought in the First World War.

3 The Egyptian pyramids were built over four ____________(s) ago.

4 The dinosaurs became extinct ____________(s) ago. The ____________ of the Dinosaurs came to an end about 60 million years ago.

5 It's strange how certain ____________(s) seem to acquire names. What came after the 'swinging sixties'?

6 Sometimes very ugly buildings are protected simply because they are of ____________ interest.

7 Archaeologists today have a much better understanding of the ____________ of humanity, before there were any ____________ records.

8 It happened in the twinkling of an eye; it took just a(n) ____________ of a(n)____________.

9 Thank you for helping me in my ____________ of need.

10 The judgment of the Supreme Court made legal ____________. It was a(n)____________ decision.

11 The sixteenth ____________ was a very turbulent ____________ of ____________.

12 My life was so different then. It all seems ____________(s) away now.

Words with *-spect*

*Each masterpiece features **perspective*** (line 17), *... humanity's future **prospects*** (line 35), *The paintings are **spectacular*** (line 35).

Use these words containing the root ***-spect*** to replace the words in italics in the sentences. Make any grammatical changes that are necessary.

aspect	introspective	prospect	retrospect
inspect	perspective	prospective	spectacle
		respect	

1 He's *looking* for gold.

2 With *hindsight* I think we should have taken more precautions.

3 You should *look up to* your elders.

4 Rupert was a very *inward-looking* child.

5 She always behaved badly and *attracted attention to* herself.

6 Several *possible* buyers have already *looked over* the property.

7 His book suggests he has a very odd *way of looking at* life.

8 There's one *facet* of his character that I really don't like: his arrogance.

"ADVANCED VOCAB. IN CONTEXT" WATSON (GEORGIAN PRESS) 1997

6 A more efficient way to learn

VOCABULARY CHECK

Choose the correct definitions of these words and expressions.

1 If something is described as *constituent* it is a) a part of a greater whole b) complete in itself.

2 If something is *segmented* it a) consists of one part and is indivisible b) consists of several parts.

3 If someone is *disadvantaged* they a) do not enjoy the conditions that others might consider normal. b) do not provide normal conditions for others.

4 A *chunk* is a) a fraction b) a piece.

5 A *neurological* disease is one that affects a) the muscles and the joints b) the brain or the nervous system.

6 *Prose* is written language a) in the form of verse or poetry b) which is not in verse.

7 *IQ* is a measure of intelligence. The letters stand for 'intelligence _____'. a) quota b) quotient c) quantity

8 *Educationists* are people who a) believe strongly in education b) study and specialise in education.

9 If you *override* something you a) prevent some mechanism from operating b) drive past it.

10 The *fast track* is a) the part of a road where you drive if you want to pass slower vehicles b) a quick, more competitive route to your goal.

Hyphenated words

Join items from each box with a hyphen to form new words. Then use the words to complete the sentences.

double-	left-	non-
fast-	long-	under-

hand	quick	threatening
perform	term	tracking

1 I wrote URGENT on it because I wanted it to be delivered in ___________ time.

2 Students who ___________ will have to do the course again.

3 I know what you want to do in the immediate future, but what are your ___________ plans?

4 This school has adopted ___________ as a way of teaching the brightest pupils.

5 These animals are easily frightened, so you must approach them in a ___________ way.

6 Our house is on the ___________ side of the street as you approach from the main road.

COLLOCATION

Verb phrases

Use these verbs to complete the sentences.

achieve	employ	quicken	work
acquire	improve	suggest	

1 How can I ___________ my potential?

2 I want to ___________ more knowledge.

3 What does the research ___________?

4 What techniques should we ___________?

5 I need to ___________ my score.

6 How can we ___________ the pace?

7 How does the brain ___________?

Lexical sets

Find pairs of nouns which are associated with each other in some way and could therefore be used in the same context. They may be similar, complementary or contrasting.

knowledge	parts	diagram	overview
language	picture	exam	poem
liver	song	lungs	skills
panic	test	number	stress

Find pairs of descriptive words or expressions (and one group of three) which are similar, complementary or contrasting, and could therefore be used together in the same context. Then use individual words to complete the sentences.

auditory	musical	non-threatening	visual
bright	neurological	psychological	whole
constituent	pleasant	with learning difficulties	

1 They could find neither ___________ nor ___________ explanation for his loss of memory.

2 Even if its surroundings are ___________ and ___________, a baby will still miss its mother terribly if she is absent for too long.

3 Babies need plenty of ___________ or other ___________ stimulation as well as ___________ experience.

4 Children who are very ___________ need just as much attention as those ___________.

5 The ___________ thing is made up of several ___________ parts.

Adverbs

Use these adverbs to complete the sentences. There is one more than you need.

commonly	dramatically	exclusively	particularly	seriously	widely

1 Her condition improved ___________ once she began the treatment.

2 The group was ___________ successful in France.

3 His fitness course is ___________ used throughout the United States.

4 The intelligence quotient is ___________ known as IQ.

5 Arnold was ___________ disadvantaged as a child.

VOCABULARY IN CONTEXT

Complete the newspaper article, using one of these words for each space. You will need to change the form of some of the verbs. Use each word once only.

Nouns		*Adjectives*	*Adverbs*	*Verbs*
approach	methods	auditory	commonly	achieve
body	notes	constituent	dramatically	acquire
capability	overview	double-quick	particularly	become
class	pace	expensive	seriously	employ
concepts	poem	human	widely	last
diagram	programme	maximum		learn
difficulties	projects	non-threatening		recall
educationists	research	preferred		start
emphasis	scores	secondary		suggest
exam	section	visual		transfer
language	stress	whole		work

How to be smarter with the same brain

We've all seen the adverts. Improve your IQ, learn a language in __________ time – it's as simple as ABC. But can you really __________ smarter or __________ more quickly with the same brain? And, if you can, why don't schools __________ the same techniques?

The fact is that more and more schools are using accelerated learning approaches because the techniques can __________ improve learning __________, based as they are on neurological and psychological __________ into how the brain __________, how it __________ new knowledge, understanding and skills and how it __________ what it has learned.

Accelerated learning draws together the work of psychologists and __________ around the world, most of whom __________ from the frightening conviction that almost all children in school, from the brightest to those with learning __________, seriously under-perform.

American research __________ that early intensive education can improve IQ __________ by up to 30 points. Accelerated learning does not mean fast-tracking very bright pupils. It is an __________ to learning that quickens the __________ and absorption of learning for all abilities. Accelerated learning __________ are not difficult or __________ and can be used in any classroom.

The __________ brain is segmented. There is a __________ concerned with survival, which can override everything else if it is stimulated, and another concerned with emotion. If you panic, or are under __________, you do not have any capacity to learn at the same time. So accelerated learning techniques put a lot of __________ on creating a pleasant, __________ environment for students.

Another part of the brain deals with long-term memory. If learning is to __________ longer than the next test or __________, it has to be __________ to the long-term memory. __________ and musical clues can help. Many people find it easier to recall a song or a __________, a picture or a __________ than a chunk of prose.

Another two segments of the brain, __________ known as the left-hand and right-hand brain, deal with the mechanics of learning. The left deals with language, mathematics, logic and linearity, and it tends to learn bottom up. In other words, if it were learning about the human __________ in biology it would prefer to start with the __________ parts, like the lungs and the liver, and build up to the __________ organism. Meanwhile the right-hand brain deals with spatial __________, music, images, imagination. It prefers to learn by moving from the __________ to the constituent parts.

According to Professor Howard Gardner, of Harvard University, there are three ways of learning – the visual, the auditory and the kinaesthetic (concerned with touch and action) – and you __________ your __________ potential by using all three. *Sesame Street*, the television __________ for preschoolers, used a brilliant mix of the visual and the __________ in cartoons and sketches, to teach basic __________ and number.

Traditionally, particularly in __________ schools, the emphasis has been on listening, reading and making __________. But in an average __________, many children will be __________ disadvantaged if their __________ visual and kinaesthetic approach is ignored.

Accelerated learning __________ have been tried out extensively in the United States, New Zealand and some European countries. Accelerated methods for learning languages have been __________ successful and are __________ used in industry and in universities. Increasingly schools in the UK are finding that they, too, can learn from the accelerated approach.

FURTHER PRACTICE

Matching

Match each point on the left with the appropriate continuation, A – F.

THE ACCELERATED APPROACH – A QUICK GUIDE

1 Children cannot learn if they feel stressed or threatened.

2 Children will not learn if they have low self-esteem and lack confidence.

3 Children need to be able to see what's in it for them.

4 Children learn in different ways.

5 There are proven methods to make sure knowledge is transferred from the short-term to the long-term memory.

6 Children's attention span is limited: even adults find it hard to concentrate for more than 25 minutes at a time.

A Lessons must include learning through sight, sound and touch.

B Learning needs to have easily understood targets attainable within a reasonable time.

C Teachers need to reassure and encourage them all the time.

D The classroom must be a warm and welcoming place.

E Learning should therefore be broken down into 'chunks' with regular breaks for reinforcement and refreshment.

F These involve reviewing what has been learnt, using visual imagery for abstract concepts, and combining words and music so both sides of the brain are involved.

Verbs with *-en* and *en-*

... *the frightening conviction* (line 9), *quickens the pace* (line 13), *non-threatening* (line 18).
In words like *frighten, quicken*, and *threaten,* the letters ***-en*** are added to an adjective or noun to make a verb. This is a common pattern. In some cases the verb begins with ***en-***.

Make verbs like this from these root words, and use them to complete the sentences.

danger	large	loose	rich	slave	title
fat	long	rage	slack	tight	trap

1 He says wine ____________ the tongue and makes you say things you later regret.

2 The apparently ungrateful attitude of the young often ____________ the older generation.

3 The Chancellor of the Exchequer said we would have to ____________ our belts and cut down on luxuries.

4 Doctors agree that smoking ____________ your health.

5 His latest book is ____________ *Time and Time Again.*

6 I simply can't lost weight. Everything I eat seems to be ____________.

7 The police agents infiltrated the drugs ring in order to ____________ the main dealers.

8 I want to have this photograph ____________.

9 Business always ____________ in the winter, and picks up again in the spring.

10 Their diet is poor in vitamins. They need to ____________ it with fresh fruit and vegetables.

11 The first colonists ____________ much of the native population.

12 They've ____________ the course since I did it. It only took two years in my day.

Review 1 (Units 1-6)

Complete these sentences with the most appropriate words from Units 1 to 6. Sometimes the initial or final letters are given to help you.

UNIT 1

1 They still have a ________ ________ of work to do on the project but not a great deal so it should soon be finished.

2 We can't lay down universal rules; each **i**________ ________ must be treated on its own merit.

3 We're not supposed to receive personal calls during office hours, so you'd better call me in my ________ ________ between 12.30 and 1.15.

4 George, don't do that. Stop pulling your sister's hair. You're a very ________**y** ________.

5 The bank's profits were down this year. They wrote off two million pounds worth of ________ ________**s** which they decided they would never be able to recover.

6 His wife is on the board of directors, isn't she? If you think he bought shares in the company because he had inside information you should report your suspicions to the ________ ________.

7 Even if he didn't ________ the **c**________ himself he probably knows who the guilty party is and could be accused of withholding evidence.

8 Many banks nowadays offer free gifts to young people to encourage them to ________ an ________.

9 I'm afraid the book doesn't appear to have come in yet, sir. It usually takes about ten days. When exactly did you ________ the ________?

10 Fresh evidence has recently ________ to ________ which suggests that more people were involved than was originally thought.

UNIT 2

1 This new fashion is the ________ ________ among teenagers but it probably won't last long.

2 People who were bitten by the ________ ________ could at last take advantage of cheaper air fares.

3 His success was reported in the newspapers but not on the ________ **p**________, so many people didn't read about it at all.

4 It was at the Earth Summit in Rio that the industrialised countries made the **cr**________ **d**________ to reduce the amount of CFCs being introduced into the atmosphere.

5 They ________ on the ________ of running cars on sugar. It would certainly solve the problem of their fuel shortage if it worked.

6 I didn't understand a word of what she said. I haven't the ________ ________ what she was talking about.

7 ________ to **e**________ who have been investigating the wreckage, the explosion was caused by a bomb.

8 No one could deny that her success was ________**ly** ________: she had worked hard for it all her life.

9 He isn't well and doesn't go out much these days. He's been in ________**r** **h**________ever since his heart attack last year.

10 The doctors say she's still very ill, but she is ________**ing** ________**s** of improvement.

UNIT 3

1 It's very noisy living next to a ________ **s**________, but it'll be nice when the new block is finished.

2 People say that certain big opera stars have made ________ **m**________ much more popular than it used to be.

3 There's a very **s**________ ________ in a tribe of chimpanzees, with one dominant male at the top and the one he has deposed at the bottom.

4 It's quite an egalitarian company. Very few of the top management are allowed to travel first class; most of the **s**________ ________ have to travel economy like the rest of the staff.

5 She made her name as a **f**________ ________ when she started specialising in wedding dresses for filmstars.

6 The referee usually ________**s** a ________ to decide which team should kick the ball first.

7 It's not easy to **m**________ a ________ as an inventor. Most don't usually earn much money from their inventions.

8 Instead of running two separate businesses in competition with each other they decided to **f**________ a ________.

9 Even if you ________ to the ________ that human beings are basically selfish, I think you have to agree that they are also capable of amazing acts of self-sacrifice.

10 Things aren't working out quite as we had expected. We'll have to go back to the ________ ________ and revise our plans.

UNIT 4

1 We used to think he was a **b**__________ __________ – a second Einstein – but he didn't take his studies seriously enough and turned out no better than average.

2 Fear of crime is much more common among old people than in the **g**__________ __________**ion**, even though the old are statistically in less danger.

3 Many people who work in science have hobbies in the __________ __________**s** such as painting or music.

4 In the **f**__________ __________**is**, since the country is a dictatorship, all power lies in the hands of one man.

5 As his immune system became weaker, he suffered one **b**__________of __________ after another.

6 They are still __________**ing** for __________**s** at the scene of the crime but have not yet found any evidence.

7 We need to __________ the **g**__________ between different groups in the community and bring them together so that they understand each other better.

8 Everyone thought the opposition party would win the election, but **c**__________ to __________ the government was returned to power with an increased majority.

9 Perhaps it was guilt that made him feel anxious, but all the way home he had the __________**y** __________ that he was being followed.

10 He's such an __________ __________ you never know when to believe him.

UNIT 5

1 Getting a business loan from the bank is a bit like finding a wife used to be: they won't accept you unless you can convince them that your __________**e** __________**s** are good.

2 Politicians should pay more attention to the __________ __________**ic**: they should find out what ordinary people think, instead of listening to big business all the time.

3 By studying these archaeological remains they are gradually building up a **c**__________ __________ of what life was like in the Bronze Age.

4 People have sometimes suggested that the plays of William Shakespeare were actually written by someone else, and they think there might be a **c**__________ to this **m**__________ in Shakespeare's grave .

5 They're not absolutely identical but they're **a**__________ the __________.

6 It was truly a **h**__________ **m**__________ when after twenty years of terrorism and war the two leaders shook hands at the United Nations.

7 Romantic fiction is not taken seriously by professors of English literature, and many popular novelists are unknown in __________**c** __________**s**.

8 The literary establishment was __________ into **t**__________ when it was revealed that the prize-winning novel had been written by a child of eleven.

9 It's amazing how many famous painters showed no __________ __________**y** whatsoever when they were children.

10 She was dying of a very rare disease and she decided to leave her body to science for __________ __________**s**.

UNIT 6

1 I want to get a job on a cruise ship for the next four months but I haven't got any **l**_____-_____ __________**s**. I've no idea what I'll do after that.

2 The purpose of accelerated learning techniques is to __________**en** the **p**__________ of learning, with the result that more can be learnt in the time available.

3 At school you can **a**__________ **k**__________ about the world, but there is no substitute for real life experience.

4 The purpose of education is not to produce a well-educated élite but to enable each individual to **a**__________ his or her maximum __________.

5 His condition has __________ **d**__________ in the last few days and he hopes to be discharged from hospital by the end of the week.

6 Bovine spongiform encephalopathy or BSE is **c**__________ __________as mad cow disease.

7 Some children are **s**__________**ly** __________**ed** at school because they get no encouragement at home.

8 I'm going to have to **t**__________ my __________: I'll soon fall into debt if I don't start to economise.

9 News programmes never stay on the same subject for very long, because people can't concentrate on one thing for more than a few minutes; their __________ __________ is extremely short.

10 It's much easier to describe physical objects than it is to define __________ **c**__________ such as justice and truth.

7 The increasing dangers of tuberculosis

VOCABULARY CHECK

Match these words with their definitions. Then use some of the words to complete the sentences, changing the form if necessary.

fuel	**a** to get worse
germ	**b** to breathe in
dwarf	**c** with justification
launch	**d** to encourage something to grow
inhale	**e** to introduce something to the public
strain	**f** a small organism that causes a disease
epidemic	**g** impossible to treat with available medicines
focus on	**h** to make something look small or insignificant
complacency	**i** an unjustified or unwise feeling of satisfaction
deteriorate	**j** to pay particular attention to something
legitimately	**k** a type or variety (of plant or disease)
drug-resistant	**l** the occurrence of a disease in a large number of people at the same time

1 The skyscraper ___________ all the buildings around it.

2 Her husband's hatred was ___________ by jealousy.

3 The doctors said that the disease was becoming increasingly ___________ and we would soon have a(n) ___________ unless other measures were taken. They said the situation was already ___________ and accused the Minister of Health of ___________.

4 The so-called 'green revolution' was the result of new ___________s of wheat and new fertilizers.

COLLOCATION

Adjectives and nouns

Combine these adjectives and nouns to form suitable phrases. Then use the phrases to complete the sentences.

urgent	system
closed	course
six-month	treatment
drug-resistant	environment
effective	problem
immune	strain

1 She went on a(n) ___________ to study journalism.

2 It is relatively easy to catch certain diseases if you are in a(n) ___________ with people who already have the disease.

3 There is no ___________ for this disease since it developed a ___________.

4 HIV is a virus that attacks the human ___________ .

5 This is the most ___________ facing us today.

Verb phrases

Use these verbs to complete the sentences, changing the form if necessary.

launch	dwarf	mark	catch	inhale
spread	focus	take	face	increase

1 How are they planning to ___________ the anniversary?
2 When you ___________ drugs there are often side-effects.
3 It is relatively easy to ___________ tuberculosis.
4 He held his breath for fear of ___________ germs.
5 Fear of dying ___________ all other fears.
6 The government held a special news conference to ___________ the report on crime.
7 The report ___________ on street crime – particularly mugging and theft from cars.
8 The problem ___________ us is so serious that we must consider all the options.
9 The number of deaths from tuberculosis has ___________ in recent years.
10 The disease is ___________ rapidly.

Prepositions

Use these phrases containing prepositions to complete the sentences. There is one more than you need.

about tuberculosis	of the risk	in population
from tuberculosis	at risk	of disease

1 Doctors warn ___________ of infection.
2 There are more deaths ___________ nowadays, partly because of the increase ___________.
3 But more people are also ___________, and they have good reason to be concerned ___________.

VOCABULARY IN CONTEXT

Complete the newspaper article, using one of these words or phrases for each space. You will need to change the form of some of the verbs. Use each word or phrase once only.

Nouns	*Adjectives and Participles*		*Verbs*	*Others*
complacency	biggest	immune	catch	at
epidemic	closed	incurable	deteriorate	ever
germ	concerned	launched	finish	from
globe	continued	past	focus	in
increase	dwarfing	related	hide	over
number	effective	six-month	mark	since
person	expensive	taking	spread	up to
population	facing	urgent	treat	
programme	global		warn	
reports				
strains				

Asbestos: Pollution, disease and complacency

VOCABULARY CHECK

Match these words with their definitions. Then use some of the words to complete the sentences, changing the form if necessary.

asbestos	**a**	breathing in
belated	**b**	delayed; late
bronchitis	**c**	very determined, persistent
hysteria	**d**	impossible to destroy
dogged	**e**	to publicise (someone's faults)
expose	**f**	uncontrolled excitement, fear or other emotion
indestructible	**g**	the act of officially accusing someone in a court of law
inhalation	**h**	a material often used in buildings because it does not burn
miracle	**i**	an unusual event which seems to go against the laws of nature
prosecution	**j**	a disease in which the tubes from the throat to the lungs become infected

1 People never stop hoping for a(n) ___________ cure for cancer.

2 Doctors face ___________ if they make dishonest claims.

3 He had to resign from the government when he was ___________ as a liar.

4 I don't like her very much but I can't help admiring her ___________ determination. Most people would have given up long ago.

5 As the volcano erupted, the villagers were gripped by ___________.

6 I thought he might have paid for the damage he caused, but all I got was a(n) ___________ apology.

7 When people are rescued from a burning building they often have to be treated for smoke ___________ .

COLLOCATION

Noun phrases

Combine these words to form common phrases. Then use the phrases to complete the sentences.

press	cost
heavy	hysteria
dogged	response
miracle	thinking
wishful	substance
official	insistence

1 People regarded nylon as a ___________ when it was first invented.

2 She couldn't afford to heat her home, due to the ___________ of fuel.

3 No one believed him despite his ___________ that he was telling the truth.

4 I'd really like to believe he's telling the truth, but I'm afraid it's just ___________ .

5 The situation isn't nearly as bad as the newspapers make out. It's a case of ___________.

6 The government deny that there's any problem. That's always the ___________ when this sort of thing happens.

Verb phrases

Combine these words to form common three-word phrases, adding an article where necessary. Then use the phrases to complete the sentences, changing the form of some of the verbs.

do	prompt	action
take	familiar	inquiry
tighten	comprehensive	assurances
follow	government	standards
set up	repeated	pattern
give	safety	study

1 We must ____________ to make sure that this type of accident doesn't happen again.

2 Everyone was very worried about the situation, even though the government ____________ that everything was all right.

3 The situation didn't look good, but we managed to avoid the worst by ____________.

4 They decided to ____________ to investigate the affair and ____________ of the problem.

5 Events ____________: no one in government would accept responsibility for what had happened and everyone tried to blame someone else.

Verbs and nouns

Which verbs are used with which nouns? Use each one once only.

carry out	mark	a prosecution	trouble
bring	do	a disease	a doctor
consult	take	the beginning	research
enforce	get	regulations	damage

Prepositions

What prepositions are needed to link these words?

1 a victim ______ bronchitis

2 insistence ______ proof

3 accusations ______ hysteria

4 to embark ______ a project

5 protection ______ asbestosis

6 adequate ______ the purpose

7 the response ______ the crisis

8 damage ______ health

9 the cost ______ failure

10 to report ______ the matter

11 based ______ research

12 a series ______ programmes

VOCABULARY IN CONTEXT

Complete the newspaper article, using one of these words or phrases for each space. You will need to change the form of some of the verbs. Use each word or phrase once only.

Nouns	*Adjectives, Adverbs and Participles*		*Verbs*
assurances	adequate	official	bring
damage	awaited	poorly	carry out
hysteria	based	prompt	consult
inquiry	comprehensive	properly	do
insistence	considerable	resistant	embark
miracle	considered	unenforced	follow
protection	deadly	virtually	get
standards	extraordinary	widely	mark
thinking	heavy		pass
victim	long		promise
			report

It took 80 years to act

The 33-year-old man who came to __________ Dr Montague Murray at London's Charing Cross Hospital seemed at first to be just another __________ of bronchitis. But then he mentioned that the other nine men who had worked with him spinning the new __________ substance, asbestos, had all died in their thirties of the same condition. When he, too, perished less than a year later, Dr Murray found the heavy scarring of the lungs that came to be called asbestosis.

The year was 1899, and more than 80 years __________ before asbestos use was __________ regulated – a delay that allowed the killer dust to be spread so __________ that most people in industrialised countries now have it in their lungs. The __________ response to the asbestos risk __________ a familiar pattern: repeated __________ of safety; a dogged __________ on proof of damage to health; accusations of press __________; a failure to __________ research and then belated, __________ -enforced, half-measures. Afterwards came the __________ human and economic cost of failing to take __________ action.

Asbestos is __________ stuff; fire __________ and __________ indestructible yet so fine and pliable that it can be spun like cloth. But its fineness makes it easy to breathe in and its indestructibility lets it stay in the lungs, and __________ damage, over decades.

Its value and danger have __________ been known. It was used 4,500 years ago to strengthen clay pots, while the elder Pliny noticed that slaves who worked with it __________ lung disease. But it was not until 1879 that the mineral __________ on its __________ conquest of the world, when Samuel Turner, a Rochdale businessman, spun 10 tons of it to lag steam engines.

The complacency and wishful __________ began soon afterwards. Dr Murray __________ on his asbestos victim to a government __________ in 1906, but added: "One hears that __________ trouble is now taken to prevent the inhalation of the dust so that the disease is not so likely as heretofore."

No __________ study of British asbestos workers was done until 1928. When this found that 80 per cent of those who had been in the industry for over 20 years had asbestosis, the Chief Inspector of Factories __________ the industry would be "safe" within a decade. It was not. The first regulations appeared in 1931, but they were insufficient and __________. In the next 38 years, while workers died by the hundreds, only two prosecutions were ever __________ .

Lung cancers caused by asbestos were reported in the mid-1930s and found to be common 10 years later, but the link was not __________ proved until 1955. Long- __________ regulations in 1969 aimed to provide __________ against asbestosis – and failed. Their "safety" levels were __________ on a single study; one of the men who did the study admitted to me later that it was "not __________ for the purpose".

A series of articles in the *Yorkshire Post* in 1974 exposing an asbestos factory where more than 250 workers died __________ the beginning of the end. The local MP started a campaign which led to a devastating inquiry and, eventually, to safety __________ being so tightened that production effectively stopped. But by then the __________ was done.

FURTHER PRACTICE

Adjectives and adverbs

Not all adverbs end in *-ly*. Conversely, words that end in *-ly* are not automatically adverbs. Find adjectives which end in *-ly* in the article on asbestos, and adverbs that do not. Then complete the sentences with other adjectives ending in *-ly*. Which ones can also be used as adverbs?

1 I wouldn't say he's ____________ but he's not very good-looking.

2 The two countries were at war for generations, but at last they are now establishing ____________ relations.

3 I'd rather read a ____________ magazine than a ____________ newspaper.

4 His condition is not as serious as it was, but he's still very ____________.

5 Manufacturers are encouraged to use environmentally ____________ packaging.

6 Why didn't you stand up to him? It was very ____________ of you to run away like that.

7 After the death of her parents she always turned to her uncle for ____________ advice.

8 The only description of him they could give was that he had a rather ____________ appearance – untidy hair, dirty clothes, and probably in need of a bath.

Compound nouns and adjectives

... *belated* ***half-measures*** (line 10), ***long-awaited*** *regulations* (line 28).

Combine ***long-***, ***half-*** or ***hard-*** with these words, or with *-ing* or *-ed* words formed from them, and use the new words to complete the sentences.

bake	draw out
earn	heart
hit	light
lose	price
range	stand
suffer	truth
wear	wind

1 After working seven days a week for a month he was determined to enjoy his ____________ holiday.

2 She made a rather ____________ attempt to help, but you could tell she didn't really want to.

3 That was a very ____________ speech. His opponents will find it very difficult to answer his charges.

4 This carpet is very ____________. We've had it thirty years and it's as good as new. And it was ____________ when we bought it – a real bargain.

5 We hadn't seen her for fifteen years but decided to take her up on a ____________ invitation and visited her one Sunday last spring.

6 He's always very ____________. He made a very ____________ speech last week, which I thought would never end. And it was so full of ____________s I was tempted to accuse him of lying.

7 His ____________ wife shows enormous patience, listening to his silly ____________ ideas all the time.

8 When I saw him in the ____________ I thought for a moment it was his ____________ older brother, who I hadn't seen for 10 years.

9 Do you know whether this good weather is expected to last till next week? Have you heard a ____________ forecast recently?

Is there a sixth sense?

VOCABULARY CHECK

Match these words with their definitions. Then use some of the words to complete the sentences, changing the form if necessary.

gaze	**a** to aim
freeze	**b** ridiculous
surveillance	**c** to stop moving, become completely motionless
ludicrous	**d** a possible effect
phenomenon	**e** a steady look; to look steadily
predators	**f** having a particular purpose
implication	**g** a belief that is not based on reason
orthodox	**h** a close watch, kept for reasons of safety or prevention
designed	**i** to look at and examine
superstition	**j** accepted as standard; conventional
scan	**k** something that happens or exists
train (on)	**l** animals that live on other animals

1 The discoveries made in genetics have enormous ___________s for the future of medicine.

2 Many popular therapies are not recognised by ___________ medicine.

3 I know it's a silly ___________ but I never travel anywhere without my good-luck charm.

4 The house is under ___________ because the police suspect the occupants of receiving stolen goods.

5 She sat ___________ing at the wonderful view.

6 The way he looked at me seemed ___________ to make me feel small.

7 The burglar ___________ when he heard the door open.

8 He surrendered when he saw four guns ___________ed on him.

COLLOCATION

Noun phrases

Combine these words to form suitable phrases. Then use some of the phrases to complete the sentences.

living	sights
military	manager
security	cameras
telescopic	creatures
surveillance	television
closed-circuit	surveillance

1 The two countries have not yet signed a peace treaty and the whole of their common border is under constant ___________.

2 The police have set up ___________ along certain roads to catch motorists who break the speed limit.

3 The first thing he did when he became ___________ was to install ___________, so that he could sit in his office and watch what was going on in the whole store.

4 Many rifles are fitted with ___________ in order to be accurate at very long distances.

Adjectives and nouns

Combine these adjectives and nouns to form suitable phrases. Then use the phrases to complete the sentences. Do not use any word more than once.

great	sense
random	study
strong	chance
orthodox	advantage
profound	scientists
scientific	implications

1 He wanted to make a ____________ of telepathy, but ____________ just laughed at him.
2 They said that whatever he thought he might discover, it would simply be the result of ____________.
3 They had the ____________ of controlling all the universities, so he was never able to carry out his research.
4 If we could ever prove that telepathy exists, it would have ____________ for the whole of science.
5 Young people have a ____________ of responsibility nowadays.

Verb phrases

Consider which verbs in the box on the left are used with the words on the right. Then use the verbs to complete the sentences, changing the form if necessary.

take	detect	data	positive
gather	perform	a change	seriously
prove	pick up	results	an ability
obtain	develop	a scent	an experiment

1 He gets very angry when no one ____________ him seriously.
2 They ____________ dozens of experiments and ____________ a lot of data, but the results they ____________ were inconclusive.
3 It didn't take long for the dog to ____________ the burglar's scent.
4 They checked her blood and the test ____________ positive.
5 These instruments are extremely sensitive and can ____________ the slightest change.
6 He claimed to have ____________ the ability to slow down his heart beat.

VOCABULARY IN CONTEXT

Complete the newspaper article, using one of these words for each space. You will need to change the form of some of the verbs. Use each word once only.

Nouns	*Adjectives*	*Adverbs*	*Participles*	*Verbs*
cameras	closed-circuit	invisibly	ambushed	detect
creatures	firmer	narrowly	confined	develop
manager	great	really	designed	gather
phenomenon	orthodox	seriously	explained	obtain
photographer	profound	straight	rejected	perform
photography	random	suddenly	scanned	prove
predators	scientific		trained	
scent	sensitive			
superstition	strong			
surveillance	telescopic			

Sixth sense helps to watch your back

As the security __________ of a large company in London, Les Lay has caught thousands of people on his surveillance __________, and he is in no doubt: some people have a 'sixth sense' of when they are being watched.

They can have their backs to the cameras, or even be __________ using hidden devices, yet still they
5 become agitated when the camera is __________ on them. Some move on, some look around for the camera. "Not everybody does it," says Mr Lay. "They tend to be people who look fitter, more alert generally."

The idea that some people can sense when they are being stared at has so far been __________ as ludicrous by __________ scientists. But now researchers in England and America are taking the claims __________.

10 According to Dr Rupert Sheldrake, a biologist and former research fellow at Cambridge University, the __________ has long been recognised in fields such as wildlife __________ and military __________. "Some police teams are said to have a rule about not keeping people in __________ sights too long because suspects may sense they are being watched," said Dr Sheldrake. "I have also heard from a soldier who said that he had a very __________ sense of being watched while walking down an alley on patrol one night, and he later
15 heard that he had __________ missed being __________."

Dr Sheldrake is now __________ data on the staring phenomenon as part of a __________ study. He said: "From an evolutionary point of view, any creature that __________ an ability to tell when it is being stared at by potential __________ would have a __________ advantage."

According to Russell Hartwell, an award-winning wildlife __________, some animals do appear to have
20 such a sixth sense. In one case last year, he was watching foxes from a hide when one of them passed about 30 yards away. "As he trotted by he __________ froze and looked __________ at me," he recalls. "I was very well hidden and I'm 99 per cent sure he hadn't picked up my __________ as the wind was in my favour. I __________ do feel he could sense he was being stared at."

In an attempt to put the phenomenon on a __________ base, Dr Richard Wiseman, a psychologist at the
25 University of Hertfordshire, has __________ experiments that are __________ to measure staring sensitivity. The tests involve measuring the skin resistance of people sitting under the gaze of a __________ TV camera. The aim is to __________ any changes in skin resistance when the person is being watched by someone else via the TV camera. In four trials, Dr Wiseman __________ results indistinguishable from __________ chance. However, similar experiments by Dr Marilyn Schlitz of the Institute for Noetic Sciences in San
30 Francisco __________ positive.

According to Dr Sheldrake, positive results from such experiments have __________ implications for science. "It would show that the mind is not just __________ within the brain, but can extend beyond it." Dr Sheldrake believes that the staring phenomenon may be __________ by the idea of 'morphic fields', which __________ bind together all living __________.

35 "If creatures do prove to be __________ to being stared at, it would also show that scientists have to take far more seriously all the supposed folklore that they have so far dismissed as __________."

FURTHER PRACTICE

Sense and *sensation* vocabulary

*... he had a very strong **sense** of being watched* (line 14).

Complete the sentences with expressions with *sense, sensation*, and words derived from them.

1 It would cause a ____________ if scientists proved that telepathy exists.

2 He was beaten ____________ in the attack.

3 She's lost all ____________ in her right arm.

4 You're far too ____________ to criticism, you know.

5 The newspapers are full of ____________ stories of crime and ____________ violence.

6 I don't understand it. It simply doesn't ____________ ____________.

7 Please be ____________. Use your ____________ ____________!

8 He showed great ____________ in avoiding subjects that might cause distress. In fact he dealt with the subject very ____________.

9 We have five ____________. The ____________ ____________ is a form of ESP. That stands for extra- ____________ perception.

10 He's very amusing. He's got a wonderful ____________ of ____________.

11 She was enjoying herself so much she lost all ____________ of ____________, and it was suddenly ten o'clock.

12 It's time you ____________ to your ____________ and realised she simply doesn't like you.

13 Do you mean 'funny' in the ____________ of peculiar, or 'funny ha-ha' – amusing?

14 Lying in a hot bath can be a very ____________ experience.

More collocations

*A **strong** sense* (line 14), *a **great** advantage* (line 18), ***profound** implications* (line 31).

Intensifying adjectives are not always interchangeable. Which of the adjectives in box A can be used to intensify the nouns in box B? Sometimes there are several possibilities. Use the most appropriate combinations to complete the sentences, using each adjective once only.

Then in each sentence substitute a different adjective from box C, again using each one once only.

A	*B*	*C*
full	regret	deep
acute	surprise	sheer
complete	sense of smell	complete
spectacular	disappointment	tremendous
profound	satisfaction	enormous
utter	nonsense	total
huge	success	keen

1 The award came as a(n) ____________.

2 Don't believe a word of it. It's ____________.

3 She expressed ____________ for what had happened.

4 I thought the concert was terrible. It was a(n) ____________.

5 The film was a(n) ____________ and all the main actors became big stars.

6 The company aims to give ____________ to all its clients.

7 She's got a very ____________.

10 Feeling sad with SAD: Winter depression

VOCABULARY CHECK

Match these words with their definitions, using one definition twice. Then use some of the words to complete the sentences.

acute	**a** easily affected
psyche	**b** very severe, extreme
arctic	**c** to say what ought to be done
demoralising	**d** neither very hot nor very cold
humdrum	**e** of high quality, a fine example
mundane	**f** a change from one state to another
prescribe	**g** very cold; close to the pole geographically
neurosis	**h** to do with the body rather than the mind
physiological	**i** a type of psychological problem
susceptible	**j** disheartening and discouraging
temperate	**k** the mind and emotions
transition	**l** ordinary, everyday
vintage	

1 If you are ____________ to cold weather I think it would be inadvisable to visit ____________ countries for your holidays.

2 There was a(n) ____________ shortage of food during the war.

3 It was a(n) ____________ year for British athletes. They have never won so many gold medals before or since.

4 The ____________ from one form of government to another is fraught with difficulties.

5 The doctors could find no ____________ illness, and the psychiatrist found no signs of psychological ____________, so they ____________ no medication.

Word formation

Form nouns from these verbs and adjectives.

dark	sick	treat	mad	boring

Join these words to make new words (using a hyphen where this is indicated). Then match them with phrases on the right with either similar or contrasting meaning.

life	end	**a** working days
life	risk	**b** the amount of work to be done
week	load	**c** pitch black
work	less	**d** dangerous
over	less	**e** variable
semi-	style	**f** way of living
high-	loaded	**g** too full
change	darkness	**h** dead

COLLOCATION

Expressions

Complete these sentences with suitable words.

1 It has been the coldest winter on ____________.

2 It has been the coldest winter since ____________ began.

3 It affects us all to a greater or lesser ____________.

Adjectives and nouns

Combine these adjectives and nouns to form suitable phrases. Then use some of the phrases to complete the sentences.

lifeless	long	earth	weekend
temperate	heavy	light	solution
artificial	acute	people	workload
susceptible	human	psyche	condition
occupational	ultimate	regions	psychology

1 Do you believe the weather can affect the ___________?

2 ___________ is not as healthy as full spectrum sunlight and can even be harmful to ___________.

3 She studied people's attitudes to work and leisure. She found that when managers had a(n) ___________ they were also more inclined to take a(n) ___________.

4 Psoriasis is a(n) ___________ of the skin, which becomes very itchy and scaly or flaky.

5 In his dream he thought he had found the ___________ to the world's problems.

6 People who live in ___________ get used to the appearance of the apparently ___________ in winter.

Noun phrases

Consider the various ways in which these words can be combined to form acceptable phrases. Then use some of the phrases to complete the sentences.

record	physiological	rate	explanation
danger	suicide	blues	countries
arctic	special	effect	levels
demoralising	winter	period	term

1 When inflation reached ___________ it had a very ___________ on people whose savings vanished overnight. Many simply could not face the future and the ___________ shot up.

2 'Lapp sickness' is a(n) ___________ for a condition that affects people in winter in ___________ when they do not see the sun for several months. The ___________ is December to January. The equivalent in temperate countries is known colloquially as ___________.

VOCABULARY IN CONTEXT

Complete the newspaper article, using one of these words for each space. You will need to change the form of some of the verbs. Use each word once only.

Nouns		*Adjectives, Adverbs and Participles*		*Verbs*	
advice	psyche	acute	long	blast	feel
blues	rate	arctic	mundane	change	prescribe
danger	reasons	artificial	northwards	claim	recede
darkness	record	badly	special	drip	seize
degree	records	black	susceptible	ensure	treat
explanation	sufferers	bright	temperate	escape	work
impact	term	dramatic	ultimate	experience	
levels	vintage	humdrum	unremitting		
period	workload	lifeless			

After the gloom, a lighter outlook

SAD (Seasonal Affective Disorder) is now a recognised disease, striking almost everyone to a greater or lesser __________ in winter, and the long grey winter we have just been through in the UK has been one of the worst for it on __________.

This January was apparently the most light-starved since __________ began, preceded by the tenth coldest December this century, which has a demoralising __________ on the human __________. The weather produced record __________ of winter depression.

"There might be a physiological __________ for it," says Cary Cooper, professor of occupational psychology at the University of Manchester Institute of Science and Technology. "But I think it is probably more psychological in most cases, though some people do get it very __________."

__________ countries have long had terms for the winter __________: "Cabin fever" and "Lapp sickness" both describe a sort of madness of distilled boredom that comes over people after months in semi-__________ with nothing to do outside.

They also have a special __________ for the grey season of transition between winter and spring, when the snow has __________ in patches, leaving gashes of raw, frozen mud all over the __________ earth and the icicles __________ inexhaustibly without ever melting. That season of transition is when the suicide __________ really perks up.

In more __________ regions like southern England, there are likely to be less __________ explanations for madness than the weather. Work, for instance. "The high-risk SAD __________, from October to March, is probably the time of year when people's __________ is heaviest," according to Professor Cooper. "People are working longer and longer hours, getting up in the dark, going to work in the dark; and there are all sorts of __________ why it might make people __________ depressed."

It has been a __________ year for SAD on the other side of the Atlantic. On the east coast, around New York, even if everyone there is always ready to __________ on the latest neurosis, they have also had a particularly long and __________ season of transition this year. The insight from America, however, is that this can often be cured by moving __________ rather than south.

There may be a physiological explanation for part of this, says Professor Cooper. Most of Canada is __________ with snow at the moment, and the physiological theory of SAD __________ that it is the lack of light which depresses __________ people. Hence it can be __________ by putting sufferers in __________ treatment cabinets and __________ them with __________ light made up of frequencies of a delicious summer.

However, simpler and more __________ cures may work, too. "There are other ways than going to Canada," says Professor Cooper. "Perhaps the simplest solution is to __________ that you go somewhere where there is a lot of sun." Those people with serious physiological SAD might need several breaks during the __________ period.

Any expert who __________ winter breaks in the sun must know what he is talking about. But Professor Cooper's __________ can be even more helpful than that: "I think it's about __________ your lifestyle," he says. For those SAD __________ whose condition is less __________, "it might be enough to get away for a __________ weekend to a nice hotel." Change is all most of us need to __________ from a dull, __________, overloaded world, full of __________ skies.

If none of these methods __________, then Professor Cooper, originally from Los Angeles, has an __________ solution: send people from the UK to __________ the changeless all-year-round summer smog of his home town. Then they will be thankful for an English winter.

FURTHER PRACTICE

Seasonal expressions

Make common phrases with one seasonal word and one other word before or after it. Then complete the sentences.

mild Indian	spring summer autumn autumnal winter wintry	sports chicken -clean showers	colours conditions leaves

1 Towards the end of autumn, they had a few wonderfully warm days. It was a real ____________.

2 She loves ____________, but she broke her leg skiing last year.

3 I haven't been out all day and I'm exhausted. I spent the whole day ____________ing.

4 I'm not sure how old she is but she's no ____________. In fact when you think about it she must be getting on for sixty.

5 They decided not to go by car because of the ____________ on the mountain roads.

6 She likes ____________. Her bedroom is all browns and golds and yellows and the curtains have a design of ____________.

7 It might snow tonight. They forecast ____________.

8 It was such a ____________ that hardly any snow fell at all.

More collocations

*... special **treatment** cabinets* (line 29), *... the simplest **solution*** (line 32), *... whose **condition** is less acute* (line 37).

Add these words to ***condition(s)***, ***solution*** or ***treatment*** to make common phrases. Then use them to complete the sentences.

appalling cold easy	heart heat neat	peak rough special	terrible weather

1 People keep food for a long time in the Arctic because bacteria do not grow well in ____________.

2 If it works that will be a very ____________ – economical and amazingly simple.

3 He shouldn't be doing such heavy work. He's got a(n) ____________.

4 I'll never lend him a book again. It was in a(n) ____________ when he gave it back to me.

5 The course of ____________ was very effective in reducing his back pain.

6 They cancelled the car race because of adverse ____________.

7 There's no ____________ to our problems but I'm sure we'll manage somehow.

8 He was hoping to enter the Olympics while he was still in ____________.

9 The prisoners of war were kept in the most ____________ and they received very ____________ at the hands of the guards.

10 She didn't offer her son the job because it would look as if he was getting ____________ .

11 How to help elephants survive

VOCABULARY CHECK

Match these words with their definitions. Then use some of the words, in the appropriate form, to complete the sentences.

bush	**a** to use
cull	**b** to grow well
delinquent	**c** faulty, not working properly
deplete	**d** to reduce greatly the size or amount of something
deploy	**e** having women (or mothers) as the leaders
dysfunctional	**f** behaving in an unacceptable or criminal way
matriarchal	**g** to hunt and kill animals illegally or without permission
poach	**h** an area of land covered with natural vegetation, where few people live
thrive	**i** to control the size of an animal population by selective killing

1 ____________ children often come from ____________ families.

2 I didn't really expect the plant to survive being moved from one garden to another, but in fact it's now ____________.

3 They were attacked by a farmer who claimed they had been ____________ on his land.

4 One of the main problems is that we are ____________ the earth's natural resources.

Definitions

Complete these definitions.

1 A group of animals such as cows or elephants is called a ____________.

2 Young cows or elephants are called ____________.

3 Someone who looks after an old people's home, a public park or a car parking area can be called a ____________.

4 A group of criminals, or of teenagers, can be called a ____________.

5 A quantity that you have in excess is called a ____________.

6 Something that you buy is a ____________.

Word formation

Join these words and prefixes to make new words. Then match the new words with their meanings, and use them to complete the sentences.

over	field	**a** spectator
infra	life	**b** away
on	see	**c** animals
a	looker	**d** sound waves that are inaudible to humans
wild	sound	**e** supervise

1 They never travel far ____________, seldom venturing more than ten kilometres or so from their village, so they are unfamiliar with some of the ____________ just across the river.

2 I don't understand why there are always so many ____________s at the scene of an accident.

3 Earthquakes produce ____________ which is inaudible to humans, but which certain animals can hear.

4 The UN ____________s the transport of aid to civilians affected by war.

COLLOCATION

Verb phrases

Complete the sentences with these verbs, in the appropriate form.

extend co-ordinate search issue pay restore keep

1 Please ___________ attention while I ___________ instructions. Otherwise we'll find it very difficult to ___________ our movements later.
2 The police were called in to ___________ law and order, but they simply couldn't ___________ the crowd under control.
3 The tiny country was so overpopulated it was constantly ___________ for ways to ___________ its boundaries.

Noun phrases

Combine words from each box to form suitable phrases. Then use the phrases to complete the sentences.

adjacent	juvenile
African	rich
annual	soft
attitude	stable
game	strict
high	tremendous

bush	land
cull	option
delinquent	population
density	problem
disciplinarian	reserve
distance	vocabulary

1 He wanted to extend the building onto the ___________.
2 He's not an easy man to get on with. He has a real ___________.
3 Whatever we decide to do will be difficult. There is no ___________.
4 You can travel a(n) ___________ in the ___________ without meeting another human being.
5 She has a very ___________ and expresses herself with great precision.
6 If all animals in a(n) ___________ are protected, it is difficult to maintain a(n) ___________. When numbers of certain animals reach a(n) ___________, a(n) ___________ may become necessary.
7 Sarah's father was a(n) ___________, but her mother was very easy-going. Each blamed the other for turning her into a(n) ___________.

VOCABULARY IN CONTEXT

Complete the article, using one of these words or phrases for each space. You will need to change the form of some of the verbs. Use each word or phrase once only.

Nouns		*Adjectives and Adverbs*		*Verbs*	
attention	park	adjacent	juvenile	co-ordinate	oversee
bunch	poachers	afield	rich	cost	reach
bush	population	alone	soft	deploy	restore
consequence	practice	annually	stable	double	search
culling	problems	audible	still	extend	stand up to
distance	purchases	distant	strict	form	take
females	range	existing	surplus	hide	terrorise
game	wardens	few	tight	issue	travel
herds	way	fully	younger	keep	weigh
order		high			

An elephantine problem

Elephants are one of the world's slowest-breeding animals; yet left to themselves, their population can __________ every 15 years. South Africa's National Parks Board, the body responsible for __________ the country's __________ reserves, knows this. Although elephant __________ in countries farther north have been depleted by __________, those in South Africa – where poaching is __________ under much better control – have thrived. So to keep the elephant __________ stable in the country's largest national __________, the Kruger, its herds have been culled __________ for the past 28 years.

To many onlookers such __________ seems both cruel and unnecessary. As a __________, groups such as the International Fund for Animal Welfare (IFAW) have been __________ for ways to stop the culling. In __________, this means either moving __________ elephants to other places, or buying new land __________ to the parks to let them wander farther __________. Indeed, IFAW has offered $2.5m to the National Parks Board for such land __________ .

Eventually, though, if the population in the Kruger is to remain __________ without culling – or, indeed, if the numbers in other parks __________ densities that are too __________ – many more elephants may have to be moved out every year.

Even ignoring the large amount of money this would __________, it is not a __________ option. Moving elephants can be quite traumatic. Until recently, shifting adult elephants, who can __________ up to four tonnes, was impossible. The equipment could not __________ their objections. So only the __________ elephants could be transported. Even today moving adults is difficult. But elephant society is __________ knit. If an entire family group is not moved together, the calves that do move can end up as __________ delinquents – as the __________ of several private game parks that have imported young elephants to start off their herds have discovered to their cost. A __________ of dysfunctional adolescents with no social graces and serious attitude __________ can be troublesome for a park. They __________ gangs; they __________ other wildlife; and, to cap it all, they __________ from the tourists.

There is now a __________ around this problem: move some adults too. In particular, moving a few __________ grown females, even if they are unrelated to any of the youths, soon __________ law and __________. For elephants are matriarchal. Their herds are organised around __________, who __________ instructions and __________ movements. Mature males tend to leave the herd and live __________.

Matriarchs are __________ disciplinarians. Only 30% of what elephants say is __________ to people – the rest of their conversation is below the __________ of human hearing. But females have a __________ vocabulary for bossing their groups around, and they __________ it often. (Males, by contrast, are creatures of __________ words).

Since infrasound can travel a tremendous __________, elephants do not get much privacy. They can hear each other from more than four kilometres away, even through the buzz of the African __________. On a still, clear, warm evening, just after dark, the sound may __________ more than twice as far. Experiments have shown that elephants pay __________ to these __________ calls, standing __________ and spreading out their ears to listen. Lone males, when they hear a female in heat, will walk for several kilometres to try to find her.

For the moment, though, the arguments of humans are drowning out any throaty rumbles from elephants. Many people agree that __________ the boundaries of __________ parks and __________ new ones would be a good idea. Fewer want to risk __________ the animal-welfare money and running.

FURTHER PRACTICE

Comprehension

Read this further extract from the article about elephants. Then decide whether the sentences that follow are true or false.

The International Fund for Animal Welfare (IFAW) has offered $2.5m to the National Parks Board for the purchase of land adjacent to the national parks. It is a tempting offer. Culling is expensive. Until the worldwide ban on the ivory trade began in 1989, the revenue that it brought in from sales of tusks, hides and meat helped to cover the costs. Now, however, culling is a drain on the board's resources. But there would be 45 a significant string attached to the IFAW money; elephants (and other animals) on the land it had paid for could never be culled.

On March 29th the board will vote on whether or not to accept the proposal. Whatever decision it makes will generate enormous controversy in South Africa. The Africa Resources Trust, a non-profit group that promotes the sustainable use of wildlife, fears that accepting the money would, in a few years, aggravate 50 the problem of too many elephants. Since there would be no physical separation of elephants on the new land from those on the old, the deal might prevent culling across the whole area – should it, as the trust expects, again become necessary. For, the trust argues, as long as the elephant population continues to grow it will inevitably reach the carrying capacity of the environment and start to harm the land.

And that harm can be enormous. Elephants are able to eat just about every plant there is. When the 55 going gets tough, they simply turn to less desirable ones. A large elephant herd can convert a paradise into a wasteland in next to no time: any animal that is a bit more picky about its vegetables than a pachyderm is likely to find them gone, and to die of starvation.

Barbara Maas, a biologist with IFAW, disagrees with this analysis. She argues that the size of the elephant herd in the Kruger park (roughly 7,500 animals – one for every 2½ square kilometres) was set 60 arbitrarily, and that the herd could easily become bigger without significant environmental damage. Yet nobody knows if this is right. The Kruger is at present in good condition, with plenty of different animals and plants. There is, indeed, a chance that this is thanks to the elephants: their clumsy ways with trees help to stop the forest from closing in everywhere, and thus promotes diversity.

On the other hand, there must surely be an upper limit to the number of elephants that the park can 65 comfortably accommodate. Anthony Hall-Martin, one of the directors of the National Parks Board, suggests, as a stop-gap, testing the carrying capacity of the Kruger by allowing elephant numbers to rise in some areas. If a problem were to emerge, and there was nowhere to move the surplus to, culling could begin again.

1 The cost of culling used to be partly offset by the profits from selling ivory.

2 IFAW is prepared to give the National Parks Board $2.5m to buy more land for the elephants on condition that those that live there are never culled.

3 The Africa Resources Trust believes it will be necessary to separate the elephants that live on the new land from those that live on the old.

4 The Africa Resources Trust believes that the elephant population is bound to increase until it reaches the point where it damages the environment.

5 The Africa Resources Trust believes that the elephants will have to be culled eventually.

6 Elephants are very particular in their choice of food.

7 The size of the elephant population in the Kruger park was decided on after careful consideration so that they would control the expansion of the forest.

8 Anthony Hall-Martin has suggested that the elephant population should be allowed to grow indefinitely.

12 Farming technology: Is it a good thing?

VOCABULARY CHECK

Find pairs of words with similar meanings.

benefit	distend	gain	mixture	quest
cocktail	drawback	lot	morality	search
cram	ethics	marvel	pack	stretch
disadvantage	fate	miracle	productivity	yield

Lexical sets

Divide these words into two groups, associated primarily either with cattle or poultry. Then use some of them to complete the sentences.

beak	cage	cow	free-range
sire	bovine	cud	hen
stall	bull	cock	dairy
peck	udder	herd	manure

1 Some people prefer to eat eggs laid by ___________ ___________s.

2 When chickens are kept in small ___________s, they often have their ___________s cut off so that they cannot ___________ each other.

3 The most valuable calves in a ___________ are those that they were ___________(e)d by a prize-winning ___________.

4 Cows seem to spend more time chewing the ___________ than actually eating.

5 A ___________ disease is one that affects cattle.

COLLOCATION

Expressions with prepositions

Join words from each box with a suitable preposition to form phrases. Then use some of the phrases to complete the sentences.

vaccinated	bred
calculated	saved
crammed	open
fertilised	quest
surrounded	worried

the public	cages
animal welfare	computer
artificial insemination	a circle
starvation	disease
efficiency	manure

1 Farm animals are often healthier nowadays because they are ___________.

2 Modern farm animals do not have a very natural life. They are usually ___________ and ___________ or small stalls.

3 Crops always used to be ___________ but nowadays most farmers use chemicals.

4 He runs his farm like a business. He is not particularly ___________. His main preoccupation is the ___________.

5 Some farms are now ___________, and it is strange to see a pig or a cow ___________ of children from a school in the city.

Noun phrases

Combine these words to form suitable phrases. Then use some of the phrases to complete the sentences.

dairy	selective	welfare	countries
developing	chemical	cocktail	breeding
artificial	animal	farming	insemination
signalling	moral	obligation	device
intensive		cows	

1 ___________ activists think we have a(n) ___________ towards all farm animals.
2 Our garage opens automatically. It's operated by a(n) ___________ in our car.
3 The milk yield of ___________ has been improved by ___________.
4 ___________ techniques have enabled ___________ to reduce their food imports.

Verb phrases

Complete the sentences with these verbs, in the appropriate form, using each one once only.

boost catch grow have improve make miss produce

1 You're ___________ the point. That's not what I was saying at all.
2 He did all he could to ___________ his lot, but he died in poverty.
3 They are ___________ exactly the same crops as before, but the new fertilisers have ___________ the yield enormously.
4 How much milk do they ___________ on this farm?
5 A few animals in the herd always ___________ infections.
6 She's been ___________ doubts about the wedding. I don't think she'll go through with it.
7 I'm collecting for a new animal welfare charity. Would you like to ___________ a contribution?

VOCABULARY IN CONTEXT

Complete the article, using one of these words or phrases for each space. You will need to change the form of some of the verbs. Use each word or phrase once only.

Nouns		*Adjectives and Adverbs*	*Past Participles*	*Verbs*	
bull	farm	artificial	bred	appear	include
cages	fashion	average	calculated	avoid	make
circle	feed	chemical	crammed	boost	miss
combinations	food	developing	cut off	catch	peck
complaint	gains	free	explained	claim	produce
contribution	herd	free-range	fertilised	confront	reduce
cud	practices	higher	grown	damage	require
dairy	quest	increasingly	inspired	encourage	save
device	stalls	intensive	mentioned	have	scratch
diseases	welfare	intensively	produced	improve	
ethics	yield	moral			
		selective			

Growing pains

Take two cows. One is a marvel of high-tech farming. It lolls in the straw in a giant shed at a farm-research centre outside London. It has been __________ by __________ insemination and vaccinated against a variety of __________. Round its neck is an electronic signalling __________ which opens its personal feed-bin. This animal __________ 12,000 kg of milk every year, roughly twice as much as Britain's average __________ cow.

The other, nonchalantly chewing the __________ on an organic __________ in Oxfordshire, is surrounded by a __________ of admirers, for today the farm is open to the public. This cow was sired by a live __________. It eats no manufactured __________, and its blood is __________ from drugs. Crops __________ on the farm are __________ by its manure, not by some __________ cocktail. The trouble is that the milk __________ by this cow is more expensive than __________ farmed milk. Many visitors may be __________ by the cow's back-to-nature feeling. Fewer will buy its milk.

That is the dilemma __________ consumers throughout the world. Increasing numbers of people in rich countries __________ doubts about modern farming methods. But few, so far, are willing to give up the cheap __________ these methods have brought. Even fewer consumers in __________ countries are willing to __________ the sacrifice, for farming technology has __________ millions of them from starvation.

Though the __________ has yet to catch on in most developing countries, consumers in the rich world are __________ worried about animal __________. These groups __________ that intensive farming is cruel. Their evidence __________ strong. In a __________ for efficiency, many modern farmers stick hens in __________ so small that they cannot __________ the ground. Turkeys are __________ by their thousand into windowless sheds, their beaks __________ to prevent aggression. Pigs are confined to __________ which prevent them from turning around.

These __________ are undoubtedly disgusting. Whether animals have rights, or whether people have __________ obligations to animals, are questions for philosophy and __________ rather than for science. But science does have a __________ to make to this debate, if only to remind those who are concerned for the welfare of the animals that a shift away from __________ farming will not always __________ the animals' lot. Given complete freedom, chickens in a __________ farm will often bully and __________ at each other. They may also __________ more infections because they can peck around in each other's faeces.

Recall the intensively farmed cow __________ at the beginning of this article. It is part of a __________ bred by ADAS, a British farm consultancy, to investigate ways of __________ yields without __________ the animals' welfare. Its enormous productivity is __________ partly by __________ breeding, but also by careful, individual management.

Every week the cows are weighed and put through a foot bath to __________ foot infections. The mix of their diet is __________ by computer so that it includes the right __________ of nutrients. It is also designed to __________ the cows to eat amply (hence it __________ molasses, a bovine delicacy).

In addition, the cows are milked three times a day – more than the average in Britain. This improves their __________, but may also __________ the discomfort they feel from overdistended udders. All this treatment __________ more manpower and equipment than the __________ dairy herd, yet the profits per cow are still __________.

In sum, the __________ that high-tech farming is bad for animal welfare is only partly true. It is in danger of __________ the point that technology has also brought __________ for animal welfare and – on some farms – may continue to do so.

FURTHER PRACTICE

Adjectives

Use these adjectives to complete the further extract from the article on farming technology.

beneficial	easy	modern	natural
benign	evolutionary	modern	spectacular
deep	human	modern	wild
domestic	instinctive	natural	

Behind all these complaints about __________ farming lies an assumption which is rooted __________ in the minds of many people. This is that __________ farming is a subversion of nature, and that plants and animals would in general do much better without __________ interference.

45 The idea has an __________ appeal, especially to the many city-dwellers who long for a more __________ existence. Yet it relies on a distinction between the human and the __________ worlds which may not coincide with reality.

Many species depend on one another to survive. One way of interpreting the emergence of agriculture, some 10,000 years ago, is that humans and __________ animals have developed a mutually __________
50 relationship. Many __________ species now face extinction, but, thanks to agriculture, the world population of sheep and cattle exceeds 1 billion – a __________ __________ success. None of this is to deny the drawbacks of __________ farming. But it suggests that the "nature" to which so many people would like farmers to return is neither as __________ to define, nor as __________, as is often imagined.

Comprehension

Decide whether or not these sentences are in agreement with the ideas in the extract.

1 Many people feel instinctively that farming is unnatural.
2 Many people feel instinctively that farming is not good for animals.
3 People who live in cities tend to have an idealised view of the world of nature.
4 The exploitation of animals by humans has been a very one-sided affair.
5 Agriculture has driven many species to extinction.
6 In evolutionary terms farm animals have been extraordinarily successful.

Animal idioms

Complete the idiomatic expressions in these sentences with the names of animals or birds, and match each sentence with the most appropriate continuation.

1 You can't teach an old __________ new tricks.
2 You can argue with them until the __________s come home.
3 Trust Susan and Mark to let the __________ out of the bag
4 You've won your argument, so stop flogging a dead __________.
5 Accusing the Chairman of bias really set the __________ among the __________s.

A They could never keep a secret.
B Nothing will make them change their minds.
C Everyone started arguing and the meeting ended in uproar.
D I've never been able to get to grips with computers.
E Why go on repeating the same thing over and over again?

Review 2 (Units 7 - 12)

Complete these sentences with the most appropriate words from units 7 to 12. Sometimes the initial or final letters are given to help you.

UNIT 7

1 Some people say that the population explosion is no longer such an **u**_________ **p**_________. They say it is actually correcting itself.

2 There is still no **e**_________ **t**_________ for this disease.

3 People sometimes take vitamin supplements to boost their **i**_________ _________ and thereby protect themselves from catching colds and infections.

4 We have never been **f**_________ with a **p**_________ quite like this. Whatever we do seems to make matters worse.

5 So we're agreed that we'll have to cut our staff. But that **p**_________ the _________ of deciding who we should ask to leave.

6 You'll have to **f**_________ the _________**c** when your boss finds out what've done, so you might as well tell him. Admit it of your own free will and he might not be quite so angry.

7 It's time you stopped burying your head in the sand and **f**_________ the _________**s**.

8 It was unfair to **l**_________ such a cruel **a**_________ on her while she was out of the country and unable to tell her side of the story.

9 The news that the Prime Minister has just bought a house abroad has **f**_________ **s**_________ that he might be about to retire.

10 We were optimistic about a peaceful outcome at first, but the **s**_________ rapidly **d**_________, and now things seem worse than ever.

UNIT 8

1 It was only through patience and **d**_________ **d**_________ that she eventually succeeded where countless others had failed.

2 For years people have been hoping that a **m**_________ **c**_________ for cancer will be found.

3 I don't think it will ever happen – it's just **w**_________ _________**ing** on their part.

4 We owe a great deal to the quick thinking of our secretary, Ms Ford: if she hadn't taken **p**_________ **a**_________ the fire would have been much worse.

5 The level of negligence is a scandal. I think they should _________ up a government _________.

6 Let's make sure we've finished the work in hand before we **e**_________ on a new **p**_________, shall we?

7 I'm not surprised he failed – it was a very **h**_____-_____ **a**_________. I always felt he didn't really want to succeed.

8 The _____-_____ **f**_________ was certainly wrong about this weekend's weather, wasn't it?

9 They say this washing machine is _________-_________ because it uses less water, but I think it actually uses more electricity.

10 Despite the Prime Minister's _________**ed** **a**_________**s** that his government would lower taxes, taxation actually increased during his term of office.

UNIT 9

1 This decision will have **p**_________ _________**s** for the whole future of our company. Have you really considered what its long-term effects will be?

2 I don't believe a word of it. He's talking **u**_________ _________**e**.

3 Many people have less faith in **o**_________ _________**e** these days and like to try alternative therapies too.

4 Zoology is the study of animals, birds and other **l**_________ _________**s**.

5 I believe in some kinds of _____-_____ _________, such as telepathy, but I don't believe anyone can see the future.

6 Bruce never gets the point of jokes, even when you explain them to him. He's got no _________ of _________ at all.

7 She wasn't paying attention when she crossed the road and _________**ly** **m**_________ being run over by a bus. She's lucky to be alive.

8 Some people believe that the lines on the palm of your hand can reveal your character. Others just **d**_________ this as **s**_________**n**.

9 I never understood why she even considered marrying such a man. I'm glad she _________ to her _________**s** in time and called the wedding off.

10 The police used a dog to track down the criminal. It _________**ed** up the _________ from an empty cigarette packet he left at the scene of the crime.

UNIT 10

1 We don't realise how lucky we are to have constant access to good drinking water. There's an __________ __________ of clean fresh water in many parts of the world.

2 The doctor doesn't like to __________ __________**tion** for this condition. She says once you start you have to increase the dose regularly as the drugs become less effective.

3 Average temperatures are increasing steadily. For example, last year we had the hottest summer since __________**s b**__________.

4 I've got rather a **h**__________ __________**d** at the moment. I think I'm going to have to do quite a bit of overtime in the office.

5 As world temperatures increase, desert areas will expand and some **t**__________ __________**s** will become tropical.

6 The **u**__________ __________ to the problem of violent crime would be to reintroduce the death penalty. Some believe it would act as a deterrent.

7 Pollution in the city reached **r**__________ __________**s** last week and more people than ever were taken to hospital with breathing difficulties.

8 More people kill themselves at holiday times. The__________ __________ always goes up when most people are enjoying themselves.

9 We try to deal with everyone equally on a 'first come, first served' basis. What makes him think he deserves __________ __________?

10 He wasn't expecting to win a medal this time as he admits he is no longer in **p**__________ __________. He had a long break from training a few months ago through illness.

UNIT 11

1 The boy didn't have much of a chance in life, coming from such a **d**__________ **f**__________, with a psychotic mother and a violent father.

2 We are slowly but surely **d**__________**ing** the earth's __________**s**. Forests are disappearing at an alarming rate, and it won't be long before we run out of oil.

3 The cat spends most of the time out of doors but never wanders **f**__________ __________**d**.

4 There was unexpected trouble at the political rally. When fighting broke out between rival groups the police had to be called in to __________ __________ and __________.

5 She chose Fine Art as one of her university courses, thinking it would be a **s**__________ __________**n**. In fact it turned out to be quite hard work.

6 Tokyo and Hong Kong are cities with a very __________ population __________ – more people per square mile than most other cities in the world.

7 Even though he was a **s**__________ __________**ian** with a reputation for punishing the slightest infringement of the school rules, Mr Stanway was also a very popular teacher.

8 That boy's got a real **at**__________ __________. He takes offence for no apparent reason and makes it extremely difficult for anyone to get to know him and help him sort out his problems.

9 It is doubtful whether certain animal species would survive in the wild if we did not have **g**__________ __________**s** where they can be protected from hunters.

10 Most countries in Europe have a **s**__________ __________, although in some it is actually declining and a few governments are encouraging people to have more children.

UNIT 12

1 She's always been an animal lover and belongs to several __________ **w**__________ organisations.

2 You are under no **m**__________ __________ to report him to the authorities simply because you suspect he doesn't declare all his income and evades tax.

3 Even before the modern discoveries in genetics, farmers had long been able to produce the animals they wanted through __________ __________.

4 He claims that in modern **i**__________ __________**ing** animals are treated as if they were industrial equipment rather than living creatures.

5 Although __________ __________ in the South receive loans from the industrialised North, they remain poor because they have to pay so much interest and are therefore kept in debt.

6 It is very difficult for a poor man with a family to support to **i**__________ his __________**t**. He can't get a good job without a decent education, yet he can't spare the time to study.

7 His new business has been a **sp**__________ __________**s** and it looks as if he'll soon make his first million.

8 There are two types of **d**__________ __________: those that are kept on farms, and those that are kept at home as pets.

9 We had to stop the car in a narrow road. The way was blocked by a cow, just standing there, calmly __________**ing** the **c**__________.

10 Ever since she read about how they keep battery hens in tiny cages she eats only _____-_____ **e**__________.

13 The coming disaster of global warming

VOCABULARY CHECK

Match these words with their definitions, using one definition twice. Then use some of the words to complete the sentences, changing the form if necessary.

adverse	**a**	very small or slight
drought	**b**	to stop changing so much
drown	**c**	how often something happens
flood	**d**	the anticipation of a terrible event
incidence	**e**	additional information relevant to the current situation
marginal	**f**	a lack of harmony and a feeling of mistrust in a relationship
spectre	**g**	to cover or be covered with water
stabilise	**h**	a long period without rain
tension	**i**	bad or harmful
update		

1 They should never have set sail in such ___________ weather conditions, especially since they were fully aware of the high ___________ of shipwrecks along that stretch of the coast.

2 The dispute over the border was a constant source of ___________ between the two countries, to the extent that the ___________ of war often hung over them. But there has recently been a(n) ___________ improvement in relations.

3 According to this morning's ___________ from the hospital the King's condition has now ___________ and his doctors say he is out of danger.

Word formation

Complete these pairs of words with the appropriate nouns and adjectives.

Adjective	*Noun*	*Verb*	*Noun*
tense	___________	tend	___________
available	___________	distribute	___________
possible	___________	expand	___________
___________	environment	pollute	___________
___________	globe	emit	___________
___________	atmosphere	concentrate	___________

COLLOCATION

Adjectives and nouns

Combine these adjectives and nouns to form suitable phrases, using each word once only. Then use the phrases to complete the sentences.

heavy	massive
leading	likely
increased	global
developing	

impact	tendency
rainfall	warming
countries	loss
scientists	

1 This year's crop was lost due to excessively ___________.

2 He's one of the ___________ doing research into ___________. He's particularly interested in studying its ___________on the economies of ___________.

3 In recent years we have seen a(n) ___________ of confidence in politicians, perhaps because of a(n) ___________ for the press to portray them as corrupt.

Noun phrases

Combine these words to form suitable phrases. Then use the phrases to complete the sentences.

fossil	greenhouse	wars	controls
climate	rainfall	stress	change
computer	resource	patterns	gases
pollution	heat	modelling	fuel

1 People who are not used to life in the tropics may suffer from ___________ when they work there.

2 The main ___________, oil, is in limited supply and people fear that it may be the cause of ___________ in the future.

3 One of the greatest threats to life on earth is ___________, particularly changes in ___________. ___________ can help us to understand what might happen and shows the need for stricter ___________, especially of ___________ such as carbon dioxide.

Now form suitable three-word phrases to complete the sentences.

global	global	sheets
polar	food	temperature
major	sea	supplies
rising	river	systems
average	ice	level

4 If the ___________ melt, many coastal cities will be flooded by the ___________.

5 Even if our summers are not getting hotter, the ___________ is certainly rising.

6 Many of the world's ___________ have been heavily polluted by industry.

7 It is estimated that the world can only ever see how to feed itself for one month. ___________ are on a constant knife-edge.

VOCABULARY IN CONTEXT

Complete the newspaper article, using one of these words for each space. Use each word once only.

Nouns		*Adjectives, Adverbs and Participles*		*Verbs*
availability	level	affected	leading	adapt
change	loss	densely	less	become
controls	modelling	developing	likely	continue
demand	oceans	experienced	rapid	increase
emissions	patterns	global	rather	predict
fossil	rise	growing	severely	suffer
gas	scale	heavy	stabilised	
ice	systems	increased	yet	
incidence	wars	latest		

Global warming disaster 'on way'

Scientist warns of risks from rising sea levels

One of Britain's __________ scientists warned yesterday that it might already be too late to prevent some of the world's most __________ populated regions being drowned within a century by the sea __________ rise brought on by the burning of __________ fuels.

Southern China, Bangladesh and Egypt face massive __________ of land and the spectre of millions of environmental refugees, Sir John Houghton, chairman of the Royal Commission on Environmental Pollution, told the Royal Society last night. Even if greenhouse __________ concentrations were __________ according to UN agreements, Sir John said, the seas would __________ to rise for centuries.

In one of the most pessimistic updates __________ on the likely impact of global warming, Sir John, chairman of the UN's Inter-governmental Panel on Climate __________ and a professor of atmospheric physics at Oxford University, further warned that water supplies throughout the world would be __________ affected.

Echoing the __________ UN analysis, he said that resource __________ over water __________ than oil were a possibility. __________ for water had been increasing in nearly every country. There were already tensions in regions where major river __________ were shared between countries.

Global food supplies might not be severely affected by global warming, said Sir John. "Some regions may be able to grow more, others __________, but the distribution of production will change because of changing water __________. The regions likely to be adversely __________ are those in __________ countries in the sub-tropics with rapidly __________ populations. In these areas there could be large numbers of environmental refugees."

Forests and other ecosystems would not easily __________ to a wetter, warmer world, he said. Health would __________, with more __________ of heat stress. Diseases like malaria would __________ more common.

Without pollution __________ it was expected that __________ of carbon dioxide (the main global warming gas) would __________ from a present 6 billion tons of carbon dioxide a year to about 20 billion tons a year in just over a century. This, he said, could mean a rise in average __________ temperature of 2.5 °C – "a change of climate more __________ than has been __________ by the earth at any time in the last 10,000 years".

Most of the sea level __________ would not come from the melting of the polar __________ sheets but from the expansion of water in the __________ because of __________ temperatures.

Sir John emphasised that while computer climate __________ was becoming more exact, it was still difficult to __________ in detail on a small __________. All models of a globally warmed world, he said, suggested an increased tendency to __________ rainfall and the greater possibility of floods and droughts. The areas most __________ to be affected by changing rainfall __________, he said, were south-east Asia and those with marginal rainfall.

FURTHER PRACTICE

Vocabulary with *up-*

An *update* (line 8) is a report that contains the very latest information. The prefix *up-* may mean 'higher' or 'close to the present' or it may have no obvious meaning at all.

Use these root words with the prefix ***up-*** to complete the sentences, changing the form of some of the words as necessary.

bring	front	grade	hill	hold	keep
lift	right	rise	root	turn	

1 It is the duty of any ___________ citizen to ___________ the law of the land.

2 It was an ___________ struggle, but we made it in the end.

3 The government was overthrown in a popular ___________.

4 Many families were ___________ in the war and never saw their homes again.

5 She is very ___________ about how ambitious she is. In fact she talks about it all the time.

6 All the tenants in the block have to pay towards the ___________ of the lifts and gardens.

7 There has been a very welcome ___________ in the economy in the last few months.

8 They widened the road and ___________ it to a motorway.

9 He made quite an ___________ speech about his ideals and hopes for the future.

10 People often blame their ___________ for the fact that they lead worthless lives.

More collocations

*'... water supplies throughout the world would be **severely affected**'* (line 10).

The following adverbs can all mean 'to a great degree' but they are not used interchangeably. Which ones fit well with the participles? Make suitable phrases to complete the sentences, using each word once only.

badly	damaged
completely	defeated
densely	exhausted
heavily	injured
highly	limited
seriously	opposed
severely	populated
strongly	publicised

1 The Netherlands is one of the most ___________ countries in the world.

2 We must recognise that our resources are ___________ and will soon be ___________.

3 The car was ___________ in the road accident, but she was not ___________.

4 The rebel army was ___________ by government troops.

5 Environmental problems have been ___________ in recent years; we hear about them all the time in the media.

6 Some manufacturers are ___________ to the government's new legislation on 'ecolabelling'.

"ADVANCED VOCAB IN CONTEXT" WATSON (GEORGIAN PRESS) 1997

The growing cities of the world

VOCABULARY CHECK

Match these words with their definitions. Then use some of the words to complete the sentences, changing the form if necessary.

accelerate	**a**	to exceed, become greater than
aquifer	**b**	supplies of something that can be used
biosphere	**c**	a muddy mixture of earth and water
deplete	**d**	anything that is burned to produce heat or energy
drainage	**e**	a particular type of red-brown wood used in furniture
fuel	**f**	wood used for building; the trees that produce this wood
mahogany	**g**	a wide area of flat grassland or farmland where no trees grow
outstrip	**h**	the underground layer of rock where water can be found
prairies	**i**	the part of the earth's environment in which life exists
resources	**j**	the process by which water flows away
sludge	**k**	the earth in which plants grow
soil	**l**	to increase the speed
timber	**m**	to reduce the amount of something

1 The paths turned to ___________ in the storm and there were pools of water everywhere due to inadequate ___________.

2 Certain chemicals have ___________ the ozone layer in the atmosphere.

3 The demand for ___________ for cooking and heating now ___________ supply in many parts of the world.

4 Chemicals can be used to ___________ the growth of crops, but they can also damage the ___________ by poisoning the ___________.

5 At last people are realising that the earth's ___________ are not unlimited.

COLLOCATION

Noun phrases

Combine these words to form suitable phrases, and then use the phrases to complete the sentences.

land	urban	growth	surface
wheat	populous	mines	warming
copper	surrounding	hills	prairies
global		cities	

1 He worked for so long in the ___________ that he became unaccustomed to natural daylight.

2 Rapid ___________ first began at the time of the Industrial Revolution.

3 One of the most serious environmental problems today is ___________.

4 So many chemicals are used in the ___________ of North America that there is hardly any wildlife there at all.

5 The villagers were afraid to go out at night because they thought there were wolves in the ___________.

6 Only a small proportion of the earth's ___________ is arable.

7 Tokyo is one of the world's most ___________.

Verb phrases

Combine these verbs and nouns to form suitable phrases. Use each word once only.

burn	an area
complete	carbon dioxide
cover	a conflict
draw	forests
emit	the future
fell	an interest
pay	oil
resolve	the price
shape	a study
take	water

More noun phrases

Form noun phrases by joining words from each box with **of**. Then use the phrases to complete the sentences.

ways	films
a layer	coping
a series	the century
the quality	the rainforests
the destruction	timber
the turn	life
a stack	mud

1 She was born around ___________. In 1899, I think.

2 Life is sometimes very difficult, but we always find ___________.

3 It's sometimes difficult to decide whether ___________ is really improving.

4 We couldn't see the beautiful pavement because it was covered with ___________ .

5 The only sign that they were going to start building was ___________.

6 He's producing ___________ for television about ___________.

VOCABULARY IN CONTEXT

Complete the newspaper article, using one of these words for each space. You will need to change the form of some of the verbs. Use each word once only.

Nouns		*Adjectives, Adverbs and Participles*	*Verbs*	
connection	loads	explosive	add	fell
destruction	mines	far-flung	burn	outstrip
drainage	prairies	global	complete	pay
effect	quality	populous	cope	provide
fall	resources	shaped	cover	resolve
fuel	series	similar	draw	service
gardens	stack	stamped	emit	take
generations	surface	surrounding	excavate	
layer	turn			
lens	waste			

The greedy cities

Peering through a camera __________ at a pile of timber turned Herbert Giradet from a film-maker into a professor.

It happened in the Brazilian port of Belem while he was making a __________ of films on the __________ of the rainforest. Tracking the camera along a __________ of mahogany being swung into a freighter, he noticed the word "London" __________ on it. "I suddenly realised the impact that cities had on the world. I started to __________ an interest in the __________ between urban consumption and human impact on the biosphere."

Now Professor of Environmental Planning at Middlesex University, he has just __________ a study on London's __________ on the planet. He has found that although it __________ less than 400,000 acres, it needs nearly 50 million acres – 125 times its area to __________ it with food, timber and other resources and to absorb its pollution. "This means that, although it contains only 12 per cent of Britain's population, London requires an area equivalent to all the country's productive land to __________ it – though, of course, this extends to the wheat __________ of Kansas, the tea __________ of Assam, the copper __________ of Zambia and other __________ places."

The city, he calculates, __________ the equivalent of two supertanker __________ of oil every week and takes 1.2 million tonnes each of timber and metal, over 2 million tons each of food, paper and plastics, and 1 billion tons of water every year. In return it churns out more than 15 million tons of __________ and 7.5 million tons of sewage sludge annually – and __________ 60 million tonnes of carbon dioxide as its contribution to __________ warming.

__________ calculations could be done elsewhere. Vienna takes in so much material that it __________ 36,000 tons to its weight every day. Aligarh City in India imports 1,000 tonnes of soil daily for use in construction, affecting natural __________ and thus increasing flooding in the __________ region. Mexico City has sunk by more than 20 feet over the last century because it has __________ so much water from the aquifer beneath it. And an expanding "ring of destruction" surrounds many African cities as trees are cut down to provide people with __________. "In all," says Giradet, "cities occupy 2 per cent of the world's land __________ but use some 75 per cent of the world's __________ and release similar percentages of wastes."

Cities have always depleted the environment around them, and have often __________ the price. When archaeologists __________ Ur in Mesopotamia – one of the world's first cities – they found it had been buried by a __________ of mud around 2,500 BC, the result, it is thought, of flooding caused by __________ forests in the surrounding hills. The __________ of Rome may have partially resulted from exhaustion of cropland. "Hell," wrote Shelley, "is a city much like London – a __________ and smoky city."

But there has never been anything like the present __________ urban growth. The number of people living in towns and cities will __________ those in the countryside for the first time in human history by the __________ of the millennium. Within another 30 years there will be twice as many urban as country people.

"The future of humanity will be __________ largely by urban conditions," writes Professor Klaus Topfer, the German minister of urban development. "The __________ of life for __________ to come – and the chance to __________ conflict within nations and between them – will depend on whether governments find ways of __________ with accelerating urban growth."

FURTHER PRACTICE

More vocabulary in context

Use these participles and adjectives to complete the further extract from the article 'The greedy cities'. Notice that one word is used twice.

average	diverse	homeless	next	relative	unhealthy
better	drinking	ignored	normal	resented	urban
better	dry	increasing	official	safe	waiting
born	existing	industrialised	poor	slower	wealthiest
corrugated	explosive	inner	poorest	sunk	
dire	hard	makeshift	pulled	swelling	

Pushed by rural poverty and __________ neglect of the countryside, __________ by the hope of a
40 __________ life in the cities, tens of millions of country people uproot themselves every year to join the __________ urban slums. The migrants find no houses __________ for them, no water supplies, no sewerage, no schools – and no welcome, for they are usually __________ by wealthier citizens and __________, at best, by the authorities. They have to settle on land no one else wants, that is too wet, too __________, too steep, or too polluted for __________ habitation. They throw up __________ hovels,
45 made of whatever they can find – sticks, fronds, cardboard, tar-paper, petrol tins, perhaps (if they are lucky) __________ iron.

Worldwide, the UN estimates, at least 250 million __________ dwellers cannot get __________ __________ water and many of those who do have to rely on standpipes that run for only a few hours a day. By 2000, most children __________ in the Third World towns will be to such desperately __________
50 families. Already more than 100 million __________ children struggle to survive on the streets.

Rich-world cities have ceased to grow rapidly, but their __________ prosperity has brought its own swiftly __________ problems, quite apart from their enormous impact on the world's environment and resources. Pollution from car exhausts has raised death rates in cities all over the __________ world. Meanwhile congestion has limited traffic to __________ speeds __________ than in the days of the horse
55 in cities as __________ as London and Milan, Utsunomiya in Japan and Trondheim in Norway.

Increasingly, cities are suffering simultaneously the problems of poverty and affluence: pollution and destitution. Worldwide, more than one in every three urban dwellers – 1.1 billion people – have to breathe __________ air. Many __________ cities of the industrialised world are __________ in __________ poverty. Men have a __________ chance of living to 65 in Bangladesh, the world's 12th __________
60 country, than in Harlem, New York, part of one of the __________. It is __________ to imagine the cities long being able to withstand __________ pressures, let alone accommodating the __________ growth of the __________ decades.

15 The earth viewed from space

VOCABULARY CHECK

Match these words with their definitions. Then use them to complete the sentences, changing the form if necessary.

disperse	**a**	a copy
era	**b**	absolutely necessary
fossil	**c**	a long period of time
habitat	**d**	to ascertain precisely
indispensable	**e**	a path around a star or planet
orbit	**f**	the possible result of an action
perspective	**g**	a layer of oil floating on the sea
pinpoint	**h**	air polluted by traffic and industry
ramification	**i**	a bone that has been preserved in rock
reproduction	**j**	to move away and spread over a wide area
slick	**k**	the natural surroundings where an animal lives
smog	**l**	a point of view or way of looking at something

1 It was difficult to ___________ the exact time of death.

2 Overpopulation and pollution are two major problems of the modern ___________.

3 Our ___________ on the environment has changed a great deal in the last twenty years.

4 She was afraid of losing her job and tried to make herself ___________.

5 If you cannot afford to buy original paintings you might consider buying good ___________s.

6 It is difficult to appreciate all the ___________s of making such a drastic change in the tax system.

7 These animals are dying out because their ___________ is being destroyed.

8 The smoke soon ___________ when they opened the windows.

9 As you approach Los Angeles from the air, you can see the ___________ hanging over the city.

10 The rocket went into ___________ around the Moon.

11 Many sea birds were killed when the oil ___________ was blown towards the shore.

12 More dinosaur ___________s have recently been found in Africa.

COLLOCATION

Verb phrases

Use these verbs to complete the sentences, changing the form if necessary.

extend	pinpoint
launch	play
leave	see
orbit	take

1 If you ___________ a view that you like, ___________ a photograph.

2 They have ___________ a satellite that will ___________ the earth every hour.

3 If you want to ___________ your horizons, you must first ___________ home.

4 She predicted that he would ___________ an important role in government, but she could not ___________ exactly when it would be.

Adjectives and nouns

Combine these adjectives and nouns to form suitable phrases. Then use the phrases to complete the sentences.

live	indispensable	smog	symbol
thick	powerful	tool	warming
local	swirling	clouds	problems
global	dispassionate	observer	broadcast

1 Is this programme recorded or is it a(n) ____________?

2 I always keep this army knife in my pocket. It's a(n) ____________ .

3 Politics is not just about ____________. It's about world issues such as pollution and ____________.

4 As a(n) ____________ of the situation, he was able to form an objective opinion of what needed to be done.

5 Many people suffering from asthma died in the ____________ that hung over the city for days.

6 He looked up and imagined all sorts of fantastic pictures in the ____________ .

7 The World Wide Fund for Nature uses the panda as its emblem – a(n) ____________ to represent all the endangered species.

Noun phrases

Combine these words to form suitable phrases. Then use some of the phrases to complete the sentences.

oil	power	rain	makers
map	fossil	fuels	stations
home	launch	layer	movement
acid	weather	planet	slick
ozone	ecology	pad	forecasters

1 The ____________ predicted that the ____________ would drift towards the beach.

2 People in the ____________ often protest about the hole in the ____________, the burning of ____________, and the pollution from factories and ____________ which causes ____________.

VOCABULARY IN CONTEXT

Complete the newspaper article, using one of these words for each space. You will need to change the form of some of the verbs. Use each word once only.

Nouns		*Adjectives and Participles*		*Verbs*
acid	problem	close	powerful	become
astronauts	prophecy	dispassionate	psychological	emphasise
concepts	reproductions	entire	seen	extend
ecology	sense	granted	single	leave
forests	slick	heard	swirling	listen
fossil	space	human	taken	orbit
gases	stations	indispensable	thick	pinpoint
layer	symbol	isolated	tiny	play
map	warming	launched	vast	write
orbit	weather	live	widespread	
planet	wonder			

A new view of home

Once a photograph of the Earth, taken from the outside, is available … a new idea as powerful as any in history will be let loose.

The astronomer Fred Hoyle __________ those words as long ago as 1948. It was a remarkable __________, the impact of which we are still feeling today. Cheap __________ of photographs of our planet from space are so __________ now that we almost take them for __________. But that does not diminish their practical and __________ impact. They have become __________ tools for __________ forecasters and __________ makers, environmentalists and prospectors, global statisticians and spies. They have also stimulated a __________ of awe and __________ in millions and especially in the few hundred __________ and cosmonauts who have __________ the view first-hand. It is a perspective on our planet that makes it seem very fragile and alone in the __________ blackness of __________.

It is hard to __________ exactly when that first image of the Earth as a whole, __________ from space, was seen here. The first weather satellite, Tiros 1, was __________ in April 1960 and returned 23,000 photographs. But that and all the other craft in low-earth orbit were still too __________ to the planet to take it all in at once. They __________ our horizons, but the cameras had hardly __________ home. In 1966, the US weather satellite Essa 1 became the first to be able to fit the __________ globe into a __________ picture, from its __________ 900 miles up.

The true impact of seeing the home __________ as a tiny, __________ ball did not come until Christmas 1968 when Frank Borman, Jim Lovell and Bill Anders __________ the Moon in Apollo 8. Their __________ broadcast on Christmas Eve, according to Jim Lovell, was __________ by the largest audience that had ever __________ to a __________ voice. Their photograph of "Earthrise" from above the Moon __________ the image of the era.

By the 1970s, the image of the Earth from space had become a __________ of the new global __________ movement. Until that time, many had thought of pollution as a local __________ – a __________ smog that would blow away, or an oil __________ that would disperse in a limitless ocean. Suddenly, the Earth had limits and the image served to __________ the interconnectedness of everything on it. It was at this time that awareness grew of how acidic __________ from power __________ in one country could fall as __________ rain and damage the lakes and __________ of another nation. It was then that the possibility of global __________ as a result of the burning of __________ fuels and the destruction of forests began to be taken seriously. It was observations from space that first showed a hole in the ozone __________ above Antarctica – though it took measurements from the ground to make people believe what the satellite showed.

The British space scientist and ecologist Professor James Lovelock believes that the image of the Earth as a __________ ball with __________ clouds has become an icon almost as __________ as the cross or the crescent. Out of the images of the Earth, __________ such as "deep ecology" were born – the ecology not just of one small habitat but of all the interactions and ramifications that affect it, including the effects of humans. Suddenly, human beings were no longer the __________ observers of it all; they were part of the system, part of the planet – and, in the new ecology, they have a compassionate role to __________.

FURTHER PRACTICE

Vocabulary of prediction

*'It was a remarkable **prophecy*** (line 3).

The four verbs in the box all mean to see or tell the future in some way. Use the appropriate verb to complete sentences 1 to 4. Then make nouns and adjectives from the verbs to complete sentences 5 to 10.

forecast	foresee	predict	prophesy

1 I don't __________ any difficulties. Do you?

2 Did they __________ rain for today?

3 He __________ the end of the world and went to the top of a mountain to wait for extraterrestrials to come and save him.

4 The WHO has __________ that 30 million people will die of TB in the next ten years.

5 Fred Hoyle's comment so long ago was remarkably accurate. His words were truly __________ .

6 You never know what she'll do next. She's very un__________.

7 The meeting was cancelled due to un__________ circumstances.

8 I've no intention of changing my job in the __________ future.

9 She showed great __________ in insuring her house from the very day she bought it.

10 This month's trade figures turned out to be much worse than the government's economic __________ .

More vocabulary in context

Use these verbs – as verbs, participles and gerunds – to complete the further extract from the article 'A new view of home'.

admire	die	feel	ignite	look	prepare	take off
admit	discover	forget	last	look	remove	wait
await	falter	groan	lie	pick out	see	
climb	feel	have	lift	prepare	see	

Since 1968 more than 3,000 men and women have been able to __________ the view of Earth from space first-hand, and a surprisingly large number of them __________ that the experience has __________ a profound and __________ effect on them. (40)

The experiences of Sam Durrance are typical. He __________ in Columbia in December 1990 after no fewer than five launch delays. Among the moments Durrance __________ are the salty sea breeze on the launch pad as he __________ to __________ aboard; the feeling of calm anticipation when __________ on his back __________ the final launch command; the creaking and __________ of the whole structure as the main engines __________ and the shaking acceleration as the solid rocket boosters __________ it from the pad. Only a few minutes later, the noise and acceleration __________ away and suddenly, almost surprisingly, you __________ you are weightless. Then, at last, there is time to __________ at the view. This is the experience Durrance will never __________. (45)

"That's the one thing nobody can __________ you for," he said. "Nothing can __________ you for what it actually __________ like. The Earth is dramatically beautiful when you __________ it from orbit, more beautiful than any picture you've ever __________. It's an emotional experience because you're __________ from the Earth but at the same time you __________ this incredible connection to the Earth" – and here his voice __________ – "like nothing I'd ever __________ before." (50)

16 What can we know of Stone Age life?

VOCABULARY CHECK

Use these words to complete the explanations and definitions.

ancestor	macho	pelt	strait
forage	mammoth	span	tale
gender	migrant	spick	whack
immaculate	myth	spouse	

1. People who move from one country to another are called ___________s.
2. Behaviour which is considered to be masculine in a very exaggerated way is described as ___________.
3. The word ___________ means husband or wife and is ___________- neutral.
4. Your ___________s are people you are directly related to who lived before you.
5. When you keep a place neat and tidy you can say you keep it ___________ and ___________.
6. ___________ is another word for perfectly neat and tidy, or perfect in every detail.
7. When an idea is commonly believed even though it is not true, it is sometimes referred to as a(n) ___________ or, more colloquially, an old wives' ___________.
8. Before the invention of agriculture, humans used to ___________ for much of their food, meaning they moved about searching for it.
9. The strip of sea between America and Asia is called the Bering ___________.
10. The skin and fur of an animal is sometimes called its ___________.
11. A(n) ___________ is an extinct animal – a type of large, hairy elephant.
12. If you ___________ something, you hit it hard.

COLLOCATION

Noun phrases

Combine these words to form suitable phrases, and then use them to complete the sentences. One phrase is not used.

big-game	leopardskin
chain of	nuts and
food	out and
fragments of	plants and
gender	women and

about	hunting
animals	mountains
berries	pelt
bone	remains
children	roles

1. The archaeologists found ___________ that showed which animals early humans ate, and from other ___________ it could be seen that they ate ___________ too.
2. People assume that only the men were involved in ___________ whilst the ___________ stayed at home. But no one knows whether the ___________ were arranged in that way.
3. She doesn't stay at home much. She's always ___________.
4. Although the two villages were only a few kilometres apart, they were separated by a ___________ and the inhabitants were unaware that other people were actually living so close.
5. A ___________ would be much more valuable than a bearskin.

Adjectives and nouns

Combine these adjectives and nouns to form suitable phrases (using one adjective twice). Then use some of the phrases to complete the sentences.

distant	north	ancestors	mammoth
hairy	sole	bank	past
human	traditional	evidence	provider
latest	tropical	forest	settlement
macho		home	view
marital		hunter	

1 We don't really have much idea how our ___________ behaved.

2 The archaeologists found the remains of a ___________ on the ___________ of the river in the ___________.

3 According to the ___________ we have of the Stone Age, the male was the ___________ for his family. He is regarded as a ___________ who went out and killed a ___________ to feed the weaker members of his tribe. But according to the ___________ this could be wrong.

Verb phrases

Which verbs are used with which nouns? Use the nouns to complete the sentences.

carry out	mind	conclusions	(an) idea
discover	revise	evidence	remains
find	rewrite	fire	tasks
gather	undermine	food	theories
jump (to)		history	traces

1 At the scout camp one boy had to mind the ___________ while the others carried out other ___________.

2 They went into the woods to gather whatever ___________ they could find.

3 We mustn't jump to ___________ about the past. One day we may find ___________ that makes us revise all our ___________.

4 When dictators come to power they often try to rewrite ___________ and undermine any ___________ the people may have that life was better before.

5 He discovered the ___________ of human skeletons and ___________ of ritual sacrifice.

VOCABULARY IN CONTEXT

Complete the newspaper article, using one of these words or phrases for each space. You will need to change the form of some of the verbs. Use each word or phrase once only.

Nouns		*Adjectives and Adverbs*		*Verbs*	
bank	hunting	correct	latest	carry out	jump
cave	myth	distant	less	drag	kill
chain	nuts	domesticated	lowest	exist	lie
children	palms	dressed	macho	find	revise
culture	past	easily	small	fit	rewrite
evidence	relations	genetic	sole	gather	settle
food	remains	grateful	traditional	journey	undermine
fragments	spouse	hairy	tropical		
gender	theories	human			
hunters	traces	immaculately			

Cave women

We have long been accustomed to the idea of the caveman as the __________ hunter-gatherer, out and about all day whacking __________ mammoths while his hausfrau __________ keeps the cave spick and span. But Professor Anna Roosevelt, a Chicago archaeologist, has __________ deep into the Brazilian Amazon and discovered __________ of an 11,000-year-old politically __________ primitive __________ settlement, where the food remains show a culture based on gathering __________ and berries. These tasks, says Professor Roosevelt, could just as easily have been __________ by women or even __________. How intriguing that in the Americas of long ago, a __________ ancestress of Hillary Clinton – her leopardskin pelt __________ tailored – showed the way to the role-sharing __________ American woman so enjoys today.

Stone Age hunters and the oldest wives' tale

It is one of the most enduring images of our distant __________ – Stone Age man, __________ in bearskin, __________ home the day's kill to the __________ wife as she minded the fire in the marital __________. Unfortunately, it is also probably untrue. Not only was the woman as likely to go out __________ food as the man, but their supper was __________ likely to be char-grilled mammoth than a few __________ reptiles or birds.

The __________ of the hunter-gatherer male and the __________ female is the creation of Victorian England, according to an American archaeologist. Professor Anna Roosevelt, of Chicago's Field Museum, is reported to have uncovered __________ in Brazil which __________ the idea that 11,000 years ago man was the __________ provider.

Her expedition discovered food __________ in a cave on the north __________ of the Amazon in Monte Alegre which included small and young animals – which, she said, could __________ have been caught and __________ by women and children. "This culture didn't emphasise big-game __________," she said. "The charred __________ remains we found point instead to broad-spectrum foraging."

According to Professor Roosevelt, earlier evidence that Stone Age people were big-game __________ was used by sociobiologists "to support a __________ basis for human behaviours such as aggression and certain __________ roles." She added: "The claims of sociobiologists do __________ Victorian England quite well. That is really where the origin of their theories __________."

However, Dr Robin Boast of Cambridge University said Professor Roosevelt may be __________ to conclusions even if she is probably right. "To suggest from her finds that you should __________ the history of gender __________ – that's pushing it a bit," he said.

Professor Roosevelt's team __________ evidence of early human habitation in the __________ levels of the cave, including cave paintings and the carbonised remains of plants and animals. As well as fruit and wood from common __________ forest trees and __________, there were also __________ of bone from large forest game and fish, birds, reptiles, amphibians, smaller fish and game.

The discoveries could also mean that __________ on how the Americas were populated will have to be __________. The __________ view is that the first migrants came across the Bering Strait from Asia, __________ in the North American high plains and south-west, moving into South America down the Andean mountain __________ later. The __________ evidence suggests that a quite distinct culture from the original Palaeoindians __________ at the same time, more than 5,000 miles to the south.

FURTHER PRACTICE

Avoiding gender-specific language

In line 7 of the article the writer uses *ancestress* as an unusual feminine form of the usual *ancestor*, to contrast with the apparent 'political correctness' of Professor Roosevelt's new theory.

Certain gender-specific words such as *manageress* and *headmistress* are often avoided nowadays, *manager* and *head teacher* being preferred. In the following sentences change the words in italics to neutral words with the same meaning. Make any other grammatical changes that then become necessary.

1 If anyone calls while I'm out, just ask *him* to wait.
2 You need to be physically fit to be a *policeman* or a *fireman.*
3 Our *air hostesses* will shortly be moving through the cabin serving a hot drink and a snack.
4 They agreed *to a man* to elect a new *chairman.*
5 Every *salesman* in the company is required to meet a monthly target.
6 The evolution of *man* is a fascinating subject.
7 Dear *Miss/Mrs* Gardener, Thank you for your recent letter.
8 Nylon is a *man-made* fibre.
9 Who was the first *man* to fly across the Atlantic?
10 In 1969 *man* first set foot on the moon.

Idioms

The heading of the newspaper article refers to the idiomatic expression *an old wives' tale.* Use these male and female words to complete the idioms and sayings.

boy brother girl grandfather grandmother lord man men mother

1 Is English your ____________ tongue?
2 I'm not responsible for their actions. Am I my ____________'s keeper?
3 I've been doing this for years. Don't teach your ____________ to suck eggs.
4 One ____________'s meat is another ____________'s poison.
5 She accused the policeman of having ____________-handled her.
6 He likes to ____________ it over his younger brother, always telling him what to do.
7 It was a good old-fashioned ____________-meets-____________ story with a happy ending.
8 He was always her blue-eyed ____________ and could do no wrong in her eyes.
9 It's quite a difficult test. It certainly separates the ____________ from the ____________s.
10 All work and no play makes Jack a dull ____________.
11 He learned to sing at his ____________'s knee.
12 This ____________ clock has been in our family for over a hundred years.
13 'Big ____________ is watching you' comes from George Orwell's *1984.*

17 The man who gave us shopping malls

VOCABULARY CHECK

Match these words with their definitions. Then use some of the words to complete the sentences.

anomaly	**a** an award
crave	**b** to praise
envision	**c** starting again
hail	**d** poor conditions
honour	**e** further consideration
poverty	**f** to imagine what is likely to happen
reappraisal	**g** to consider to be at an end or no longer of use
renewal	**h** someone who can imagine future improvements in life
visionary	**i** to want something very strongly
write off	**j** an exception to what is normal

1 They were ___________ed as heroes when they returned from the war and received many ___________s, but within a few years they were living in ___________.

2 We should never ___________ the possibility of a peaceful solution to the dispute. There may be a(n) ___________ of the talks very soon.

3 Politicians ___________ed a much greater financial benefit from ending the arms race.

Word formation

Join these words with a hyphen to make new words, and match them with their definitions.

self	war	**a** since 1946
post	time	**b** complete and separate
full	storey	**c** an officer in the US navy
multi	commander	**d** consisting of several levels
lieutenant	contained	**e** every working day for normal hours

Join these words to make new words (with no space or hyphen), using each word once only.

country	main	town	land
down	market	stream	place
farm	neighbour	side	hood

COLLOCATION

Noun phrases

Combine these words to form suitable phrases. Then use some of the phrases to complete the sentences.

town	vegetable	house	development
health	shopping	mall	programmes
property	family	square	garden
training	crime	prevention	care

1 Each political party tries to convince the public that they have the best policies on ___________, ___________ and ___________ for the unemployed.

2 Small shops have found it very difficult to survive since the introduction of the ___________.

3 The ___________ used to be very attractive but it has been ruined by ___________.

Adjectives and nouns

Combine these adjectives and nouns to form suitable phrases which contrast in meaning with phrases a – g.

low	city
late	income
moral	renewal
urban	imperative
inner	diversity
racial	housing
affordable	sixties

a the suburbs
b a uniform culture
c high salaries
d expensive residences
e something unimportant
f the next decade
g dereliction

Specifying noun phrases

Insert these phrases into the sentences.

the concept of	14,000 acres of	a billion dollars in
the quality of	years of	

1 The new town was built on farmland.
2 It will take a long time for the area to recover from neglect.
3 Our modern society is based on racial diversity.
4 He set out to improve civic life.
5 The government granted loans to developers.

Verb phrases

Which verbs are used with which nouns? Join these words to make suitable phrases, using each word once only.

tend	improve	a term	your attention
coin	make	an office	a foundation
attend	turn	university	the garden
establish	run	the quality	a profit

VOCABULARY IN CONTEXT

Complete the newspaper article, using one of these words or phrases for each space. You will need to change the form of some of the verbs. Use each word or phrase once only.

Nouns		*Adjectives and Adverbs*	*Participles and Gerunds*	*Verbs*
business	profits	affordable	based	attend
care	quality	downtown	built	begin
cities	residents	full-time	coining	establish
companies	run	hard	containing	hail
development	shoppers	inner	intended	help
house	storey	late	parking	make
life	training	low	presenting	prove
mainstream	vegetable	moral	written off	run
mall	war	passionately		tend
prevention		racial		turn
		urban		
		vibrant		

James Rouse

James Rouse was a visionary of __________ renewal who developed the world's first shopping __________ in Baltimore, built new towns in the US countryside and used the profits to __________ generate housing for the poor. An anomaly among developers, he __________ believed in the social benefit of his projects and his innovations forced the reappraisal of suburban growth and __________ city organisation.

The son of a prosperous canned-foods broker, Rouse was taught to work __________, rising at dawn to __________ the family __________ garden. In 1930 his father died, leaving the family of five children with so many debts that the family __________ had to be sold. He __________ the University of Virginia until 1933 when the Great Depression forced him to work __________ and continue his degree in law by studying at night.

His first job was __________ cars in a __________ Baltimore garage. He __________ his career in 1936 at a branch of a Maryland mortgage office which he __________ until 1939 before leaving to start his own firm, Moss-Rouse Company, financing single-family homes. After the Second World War, which he served out as a lieutenant-commander in the Naval Air Reserve in the Pacific, he expanded his __________ to shopping centres.

By the __________ 1950s, Rouse was using his __________ to develop the nation's first enclosed shopping centre – Mondawmin Mall in Baltimore – __________ the term "shopping mall", and thus he created the multi- __________ mall and food court.

His most famous __________ was Columbia, a new town __________ on 14,000 acres of farmland outside Baltimore in the late sixties. __________ on the concept of __________ diversity, and __________ as a response to the chaotic post- __________ development of American cities, it was built as a self-contained community organised around nine small "villages", each __________ several hundred houses and its own small shopping area. It now has 80,000 __________.

In the 1970s Rouse __________ his attention to the inner __________ which had been largely __________ for commercial potential by developers. He envisioned the marriage of the suburban mall with the more __________ life of a city street in self-contained areas he termed "festival marketplaces". The first, the Faneuil Hall area in Boston, __________ to be exactly what tourists and __________ craved – a comforting ideal of a town square in the centre of an unfamiliar city.

Throughout his career as head of the Rouse Company, one of America's most successful property development __________, he sought not just to __________ profits but to improve the __________ of civic life.

After retirement in 1979 he began what he called "by far the most important work" of his life. The Enterprise Foundation he __________ sought to provide people with __________ incomes with good, __________ housing and the opportunity to lift themselves out of poverty into the __________ of American life.

By 1994 the foundation had granted $1.7bn in loans and grants to develop more than 61,000 homes for low-income people and had expanded its charter to organise __________ programmes, crime- __________ efforts and health __________. He held that helping neighbourhoods recover from years of neglect was not only a __________ imperative but cheaper in the long __________. "It's not enough to provide housing," Rouse said in 1991. "It's necessary to transform the neighbourhoods themselves."

In __________ Rouse with the nation's highest civilian honour, the Presidential Medal of Freedom, President Bill Clinton __________ him as an American hero who helped "heal the torn-out heart" of America's cities. "James Rouse's life had been defined by faith in the American spirit," he said.

FURTHER PRACTICE

Register: formal vocabulary

Some of the vocabulary used in the article is slightly formal, more typical of written than spoken English. In the following sentences replace the words that are in bold or italics with more formal words. Use words from the article to replace those in italics.

1 Adelaide Beecham was from a *rich* family and *went to* a private school.
2 She had a *lively* personality and became a novelist, **famous** for her **many** works of romantic fiction.
3 Her **latest book** has been *praised* as a masterpiece.
4 She *believed* that we all *want* fame and fortune and are constantly *trying* to *change* our lives.
5 She *imagined* her future home as a **peaceful place** for artists.
6 She **bought** a small *house* in the suburbs and was **given** permission to **build** an extension.
7 When she *got* older she used to *get up* very early to *do some gardening* before breakfast.

Register: words for people

Folk is a friendly, informal word for *people* – it doesn't mean quite the same as it has other connotations. *Persons* is another word for *people,* but it is used in formal, official or legal contexts.

Complete these groups of words with less formal or more formal words.

Less formal ...... more formal

1 folk people persons
2 folks ____________ kin
3 ____________ man ____________
4 ____________ woman ____________
5 lad ____________ ____________
6 ____________ children ____________
7 ____________ old man ____________
8 mate/pal ____________ ____________
9 ____________ fiancé(e)

Now use a word or words from each group above to complete the sentence with the same number.

1 a The maximum load for this lift is six ____________.
  b Hotels like that are far too pricey for us ordinary ____________.
2 a The police will not release the identity of the victim until the next of ____________ has been informed.
  b I'm going up north to see my ____________ next weekend.
3 Have you heard the joke about the ____________ with a chicken on his head?
4 She's gone out with the ____________s. They're having a hen party.
5 He's too young to go to prison so he's in ____________ custody.
6 I'm sick of those ____________s. I hate living so close to a(n) ____________ school.
7 Don't call it an old people's home – it's for ____________s.
8 a I've known him since I was a lad. We were ____________s at school.
  b They were ____________s in arms during the war.
9 She introduced her ____________ to her uncle as her ____________, although this wasn't strictly true as they hadn't actually got engaged.

A devastating Atlantic tidal wave

VOCABULARY CHECK

Divide these words into pairs or groups that can have similar meanings. There are thirteen pairs, two groups of three words and one group of four.

apocalyptic	devastation	imperceptible	side
breaker	fairly	invisible	slide
cataclysm	fall	lethal	slip
catastrophic	flank	monitor	survey
collapse	generate	plot	threatening
create	hazard	relatively	unseen
danger	huge	ruin	unsound
destruction	immeasurable	scenario	unstable
detect	impending	see	wave

Adjectives and nouns

From which nouns are these adjectives derived? Use the nouns to complete the sentences.

apocalyptic	cataclysmic	catastrophic	volcanic

1 James likes reading stories set in an imaginary future after the world has been almost destroyed in a nuclear ___________ or by a(n) ___________ caused by a collision with an asteroid.
2 He seems to enjoy reading about real-life ___________s too.
3 He never misses programmes on television about earthquakes and ___________s.

Now use these adjectives and nouns to complete the sentences.

breaker	eruption	idyllic	ridge
catastrophic	expedition	lava	scar
devastation	fracture	realm	

4 He sustained multiple ___________s in the car accident and his injuries left several ___________s on his face.
5 It was a(n) ___________ scene – beautiful and really peaceful.
6 In the ___________ of foreign policy the government's record was disastrous.
7 The ___________ caused by the ___________ of the volcano was ___________ , and the ___________ came dangerously close to the village.
8 Surfers love to ride the ___________s on the Pacific coast.
9 We're hoping to go on a(n) ___________ to the Himalayas.
10 From the high ___________ running north-south we had two contrasting views, green to the west and almost desert to the east.

Word formation

Make words to complete the sentences by joining items from each box. Use one item in the first box twice.

land	sub
mountain	out

marine	scape	side
run	slide	

1 The ___________ had been spoiled by a ___________ that had scarred the ___________.

2 We must economise. Otherwise our expenditure will soon ___________ our income.

3 Napoleon once had the idea of invading England by ___________.

COLLOCATION

Noun phrases

Form suitable phrases with these words. Then use some of the phrases in the sentences.

active	mass
disaster	potential
geological	shallow
holiday	tidal

destination	movies
destruction	volcano
fault	waters
hazard	wave

1 Many people are afraid to live in Los Angeles because it lies on a(n) ___________ which makes it susceptible to earthquakes, although there is no ___________ nearby.

2 We spent idyllic hours lying on the beach and swimming in the ___________ of the bay.

3 Have wars become any less common since the invention of weapons of ___________?

4 She loves watching ___________ like *Earthquake*.

Verb phrases

Which verbs combine well with which nouns? Make common phrases, and then use the verbs in the appropriate form to complete the sentences.

bear	blow	cause
cross	detect	monitor
present		

devastation	to pieces	changes
the scars	a danger	the Atlantic

1 He still ___________ the scars from the gunfight in which his hand was ___________ to pieces.

2 The weather conditions ___________ the greatest danger while he was ___________ the Atlantic. One particular storm ___________ devastation on deck.

3 They connected the patient up to a machine that ___________ any changes in his heartbeat. Very sensitive instruments are needed to ___________ small changes.

VOCABULARY IN CONTEXT

Complete the newspaper article, using one of these words for each space. You will need to change the form of some of the verbs. Use each word once only.

Nouns		*Adjectives*	*Adverbs*	*Verbs*
cause	fracture	catastrophic	alone	blow
changes	history	future	closely	cause
collapse	holiday	geological	easily	devastate
danger	loss	high	equally	fall
destruction	peaks	huge	fairly	lie
disaster	plot	imperceptible	literally	monitor
eruptions	realms	potential	recently	predict
expedition	scars	sensitive	relatively	present
fears		shallow	slowly	reach
flank		sleeping	volcanically	show
		steepest		slide
		tidal		visit

Lethal shockwave from an island in the sun

It reads like the __________ from a __________ movie. Florida is __________ by a tidal wave tens of metres high. The destruction and __________ of life is immeasurable. The wave which __________ so much devastation crossed the Atlantic in just a few hours, unseen until it __________ the American coast. Its source is an unstable __________ fault in the Canary Isles, more usually thought of as an idyllic __________ destination of thousands of European tourists than as the cause of disaster.

To ensure such a scenario remains in the __________ of Hollywood, a group of British scientists __________ travelled to the Canaries. By monitoring the fault which threatens to create the __________ wave, they hope to __________ any hazard long before it could happen.

In the middle of the ocean these waves of mass __________ – called *tsunami* – are almost invisible. Only when they reach the __________ waters around coasts do they become __________ breakers. The ruin caused by even a __________ small one can be apocalyptic. When the Krakatoa volcano __________ itself to pieces in the last century, a *tsunami* six metres __________ killed 30,000 people.

Tsunami can also be generated when a huge landslide __________ into the sea. This has never been seen in historical times but scientists have now identified the island of La Palma as a __________ hazard.

"There is a __________ that the side of the volcano facing west may fall into the Atlantic," says Professor Bill McGuire of the Centre for Volcanic Research in Cheltenham, who was part of the recent __________.

"It could __________ happen during the next few weeks or months or years," he said. " __________, it could happen 100 years or more into the future. The island is very unstable and this is something which could happen __________ soon."

La Palma is not only the __________ island in the world but has also been the most __________ active of the Canary Isles in the past 500 years. There have been two __________ on the island this century __________ – the last one was in 1971.

The volcanoes themselves do not __________ much danger. La Palma lava moves so __________ that most people could __________ outrun it, so there is no __________ for anxiety to the many tourists who __________ the island. The real danger __________ in the possibility that an eruption might trigger the __________ of a volcanic ridge which is unsound.

The problem started when an eruption in 1949 caused several cubic kilometres of rock to __________ a few metres toward the sea. This also opened a two-kilometre-long __________ which can easily be seen to this day. There are not only __________ that a __________ eruption would cause the rock to move again, but that next time, the landslide will not stop. If this happened, the resulting tsunami would be __________.

"There have been three of these collapses in the __________ of the island," says Juan Carlos Carracedo of the Spanish National Research Council. Not only does the landscape bear the __________ of these cataclysms, but submarine photos __________ rock from the __________ of old volcanoes far out to sea. "Another collapse is impending. The only way to prevent this hazard is to study the island __________."

By __________ the change in shape of the mountainside, the team hope not only to discover if the western __________ is slipping due to gravity, but to predict if the __________ volcano is growing restless. Before eruptions, volcanoes always swell. This swelling may be __________ to the human eye. Only by surveying the shape of the ground with __________ instruments can small __________ be detected.

FURTHER PRACTICE

Figurative meanings and more collocations

Use these words to complete the sentences. Which meanings are literal and which are more figurative?

fracture outrun realm scenario wave

1 It's totally unfeasible. It's simply not within the ___________s possibility.
2 They described the worst-case ___________, in which the whole of New York could end up below sea level.
3 She suffered a hairline ___________ of the collar bone – a crack rather than a break.
4 ___________s of pain and sickness swept over her as she waited to be rescued.
5 Alfred was the first English king to entrust the defence of the ___________ to the navy.
6 The rioters easily ___________ the police, who were hampered by their riot gear.
7 Serious ___________s have started to appear in the coalition government.
8 It is illegal to deface coins of the ___________.
9 They changed the story while they were making the film. In the original ___________ the couple were never reunited.
10 He ___________d his skull in the accident. He should have been wearing his crash helmet.
11 It is feared that demand for petrol will soon ___________ supply.
12 He isn't very practical. His far-fetched ideas always seem to belong to the ___________s of fantasy.

Isle or *island*?

Complete these sentences with *isle* or *island.*

1 The British ___________s comprise Great Britain, Ireland and smaller ___________ such as the Scilly ___________, the ___________ of Man and the ___________ of Wight.
2 If there's a traffic ___________ in the middle of the road it's much easier for pedestrians to cross safely.
3 She spent six weeks marooned on a desert ___________, building her own shelter and finding her own food.
4 'No man is an ___________' is probably the poet John Donne's most famous line.
5 Crete is the largest of the Greek ___________s.
6 The ___________ of Dogs is an area of east London. It is not actually an ___________ but is surrounded on three sides by the River Thames.

Review 3 (Units 13 - 18)

Complete these sentences with the most appropriate words from Units 13 to 18. Sometimes the initial or final letters are given to help you.

UNIT 13

1 The motor rally was cancelled due to **a**__________ **w**__________ __________**s**: many roads were icy and some were even blocked by snow.

2 The river flooded after the __________**y** **r**__________**l**.

3 Coal, oil and natural gas occur in rock formations and are known as __________ __________**s**.

4 New technology enables people to use **c**__________ __________**ing** to predict the future of a given situation, but the reliability of the process depends on accurate data.

5 The main cause of global warming is thought to be the increase of certain so-called **g**__________ __________**s** in the atmosphere.

6 Three members of the expedition were trapped in a cave and died of starvation when their __________ __________**s** ran out.

7 K2 is the second highest mountain in the world, at 8,611 meters above __________ __________.

8 We were all very surprised that he managed to finish the course after starting so badly. It was an **up**__________ **s**__________ for him but he made it in the end.

9 The king was overthrown in a **p**__________ __________**ing**. Both he and the military had no choice but to bow to the will of the people.

10 One person was killed and three others were __________**ly** __________**ed** in the crash.

UNIT 14

1 He gave up the idea of pursuing his career. He considered it a small **p**__________ to __________ for the opportunity to look after his invalid wife.

2 He used to __________ a keen __________ in politics, but these days he doesn't even vote.

3 They brought in several mediators to try to **r**__________ the **c**__________, but all failed, and the two communities are terrorising each other again.

4 Many psychologists believe that we are the product of our environment and that our experiences in early childhood **sh**__________ our whole **f**__________.

5 We cannot yet cure this disease, but with modern drugs we can at least improve the __________**y** of __________ of those who suffer from it.

6 In the future, __________ for certain metals is almost certain to __________ supply.

7 Forests used to __________ a much larger __________ of the country than they do today.

8 At least a third of the world's population live in __________**re** __________**y**.

9 In the poorest areas most families have only cardboard and plastic sheeting to build the shacks they live in. The lucky few might have a roof of **c**__________ **i**__________ over their heads.

10 Even in relatively wealthy cities, the transfer of many businesses from the centre to the suburbs has made life in the __________ __________ poorer and harder.

UNIT 15

1 They've __________ a new communications **s**__________ which will stay in orbit over the middle of the Atlantic.

2 James is very cautious, with a narrow outlook on life. He needs to **ex**__________ his **h**__________**s** and try something new.

3 She **p**__________**ed** a decisive **r**__________ in negotiating the terms of the contract.

4 The Minister doesn't like to take part in recorded programmes because the interviews are always edited. He prefers to appear in __________ **br**__________.

5 The rocket didn't even take off; it exploded on the __________ __________.

6 The older generation say that the young __________ too much for __________: they have never known real hardship, and they don't realise how lucky they are.

7 Some say the __________**y** **m**__________ started with a book called *Silent Spring*, which drew our attention to the damage we were doing to the environment.

8 Many lakes have been poisoned and forests destroyed by **a**__________ __________, caused mainly by the emissions from factories and power stations.

9 International law forbids tankers to discharge oil into the sea, yet __________ **s**__________ continue to pollute our beaches and kill many sea birds every year.

10 She was very upset by the incident at the time, but fortunately it seems to have had no __________**ing** __________ on her.

UNIT 16

1 It's just an __________ __________ tale. No sensible person believes that kind of superstitious nonsense nowadays.

2 Don't __________ to __________**s**! Just because they were seen in a restaurant together doesn't mean they're having an affair.

3 Is it sexist to say that Greek is my __________ __________, rather than my native language?

4 One of the most dramatic social changes in the west over the last fifty years or so has been the blurring of __________ __________**s**. Men and women no longer have such separate, clearly defined areas of activity.

5 Scientists had to __________ their original **t**__________**y** when new evidence came to light.

6 If we count back just ten generations we see that we are each descended from over a thousand people, and from over a million if we go back ten more. We all have common ancestors in the **d**__________ __________**t**.

7 You must get __________ and **a**__________ more. You'll go mad sitting here on your own all day.

8 Is it __________**y** __________**t** to say 'Stone Age man'? Shouldn't we say 'Stone Age people'?

9 One of his ancestors used to go _____-_____ __________**ing**, and in his house he still has several wild animal heads on the wall.

10 As **t**__________ **f**__________ are being destroyed, we are losing the opportunity to develop new drugs from the plants that grow there.

UNIT 17

1 **He**__________ __________**e** costs have risen enormously in recent years, but we need more hospitals, more doctors and better-paid nurses.

2 He runs **t**__________ **p**__________**s** for people who have to learn a new skill when they are made redundant.

3 Burglaries have increased again in spite of the new **c**__________ **p**__________ measures introduced by the police last year.

4 We must ensure that the elderly are well looked after. It's a **m**__________ **i**__________ and we cannot neglect our duty.

5 The government's programme of **u**__________ **r**__________ has utterly transformed this inner city area. It used to be full of slums, but now it's all new shops and businesses, modern flats and well-kept public gardens.

6 Many races of the world are represented in American society. There's a high degree of __________ __________**y**.

7 It's not a new television. We just __________**ed** the __________**y** of the picture by changing the position of the aerial.

8 The police are not releasing the names of the victims until the __________ of __________ have been informed.

9 All **s**__________ __________**s** are allowed free travel on our city's public transport during off-peak hours.

10 He always **b**__________**ed** __________**ly** in her talents as a writer and was convinced that one day she would write a bestseller.

UNIT 18

1 He photographed this **i**__________ **s**__________ of rural life in Baddingley just a few years before the peace of the countryside was destroyed by the new motorway.

2 He specialised in taking photographs of __________ __________**s** and lost his life when he got too close to the rim of one that was actually erupting.

3 The farm is situated on a **g**__________ __________ and you can see where the ground has moved and changed the shape of the fields.

4 Do you think the nations of the world will ever destroy all their weapons of **m**__________ __________**tion**?

5 The end of the Cold War made us all feel more secure, but it may **p**__________ new __________**s** if the nuclear weapons that belonged to the superpowers fall into the hands of terrorists.

6 Every village in the area still **b**__________**s** the __________**s** of the civil war that destroyed the lives of so many families.

7 A new wing for the hospital is simply not within the **r**__________ of __________**y**. We just haven't got the money.

8 In the **w**_____-_____ **s**__________ she could spend the rest of her life in a wheelchair, but there's a fifty-fifty chance she'll be able to learn to walk again.

9 One of the first English novels was Daniel Defoe's *Robinson Crusoe*, the story of a man who was shipwrecked and marooned on a __________ __________.

10 He's lying in hospital, attached to a cardiograph – a machine that **m**__________ any __________**s** in his heartbeat.

19 How to conquer the fear of flying

VOCABULARY CHECK

Match these words and phrases with their definitions. Then use them to complete the sentences.

an abomination	**a** *(colloquial)* drunk
an air-miss	**b** *(colloquial)* anxious or afraid
in a blue funk	**c** a near-collision between two aircraft
palpitations	**d** uneven movements of the heart
smashed	**e** uneven movements of the air
turbulence	**f** something horrible or bad

1 It shouldn't be allowed. It's ___________.

2 She's got a weak heart and suffers from ___________.

3 He's ___________ about his interview tomorrow.

4 When it's over, all he'll want to do is get ___________.

5 The planes passed so close to each other that the newspapers called it ___________, but the pilot told the passengers they were simply going through some ___________.

Hyphenated words

Join items from each list with a hyphen to form new words. Then use the hyphenated words to complete the sentences.

45	40s
mid	term
mid	minute
long	hypnosis
closed	thirds
self	air
two	in

1 I don't know how old he is but I'd guess he's in his ___________.

2 Sixty-two per cent? That's nearly ___________.

3 She always takes the stairs. If she goes in a lift she soon panics because she gets that ___________ feeling.

4 It's a miracle there were any survivors from the ___________ collision.

5 This new drug seems to be safe, but no one knows what the ___________ effects might be.

6 Each teaching 'hour' in this school is actually a ___________ period.

7 When people want to lose weight they sometimes try ___________.

COLLOCATION

Adjectives and nouns

Combine these adjectives and nouns to form suitable phrases.

vast	jet
white	space
relaxed	numbers
clinical	setting
closed-in	knuckles
wide-bodied	psychologist

Noun phrases

Combine these words to form suitable phrases. Then use the phrases to complete the sentences.

tape	rate
engine	attacks
success	noise
panic	recording
consultant	techniques
relaxation	psychiatrist

1 He made an illegal ___________ of the concert.

2 It's a lovely smooth ride and there's hardly any ___________, but the car's far too expensive for me.

3 If you suffer from stress or ___________ there are various ___________ you can try.

4 She's got an important position as a ___________ in a hospital.

5 I'm afraid the chances of a full recovery are very low. This operation doesn't have a very good ___________ .

Verb phrases

Join these verbs and nouns to form common phrases, using each one once only.

Verbs		Nouns	
play	board	a bus	a course
join	conquer	the fear	courage
take		a tape recording	

Prepositions

Use these prepositions to complete the sentences. You will need to use one preposition twice.

about by in on with

1 The show culminated ______ a magnificent firework display.

2 The depression was brought ______ ______ the death of her husband.

3 Don't you worry ______ it. I'll deal ______ it.

4 I don't know how she manages to cope ______ all those children.

VOCABULARY IN CONTEXT

Complete the newspaper article, using one of these words for each space. You will need to change the form of some of the verbs. Use each word once only.

Nouns		*Adjectives and Adverbs*		*Verbs*	
comment	psychiatrist	aged	long-term	aim	land
courage	rate	along	physically	board	lie
engine	relaxation	blue	surprisingly	conquer	make
media	setting	clinical	unlikely	control	outline
panic	tape	closed-in	vast	culminate	play
plane	trips	icily	wide-bodied	deal	run
process		likely		get	work
				join	worry

Airport lessons put flying fear to flight

Courses offer happy landings to travellers grounded by terror

Fear of flying is no joke. A glance round any __________ reveals white faces and white knuckles. Other sufferers may be __________ sick, shake, sweat, have palpitations, faint, or even have mid-air __________ attacks.

But now, attempts are being __________ to help such people cope with their fears. Captain Douglas Ord, a pilot, helps run British Airways courses for those who want to __________ the fear. He thinks newspapers and television have made more people frightened. "It is brought on by the disasterising and air-miss stories of the __________," he said.

Many of those who __________ the courses – which take a day and __________ in a 45-minute flight – have never been comfortable flying. "It's turbulence usually," Captain Ord said. "Nobody tells them what's going on and they get into a __________ funk. We __________ to get them to cope with flying."

The courses __________ approximately every six weeks. Those who attend are __________ from 18 to the mid-40s, although some bring their children too. About two-thirds are women. "Men won't go on the course. They __________ smashed and sit there white-knuckled," said Captain Ord.

In the morning, the pilot __________ the technical aspects of the flight, explaining how the wings __________, what the noises are and how the aircraft __________ with turbulence. In the afternoon, a psychologist talks through the passengers' fears with them and teaches them __________ techniques.

Dr Keith Stoll, one of the __________ psychologists involved, describes it as a "self-hypnosis de-sensitisation __________". People may be afraid they are going to be sick or scream. To help them __________ their symptoms, they talk through the journey in the classroom – from leaving the room, to __________ the bus to the airport, to getting on the plane.

"We tend to get 90 per cent to 100 per cent of people on the plane," he said. "It takes a lot of __________ to do it. Where the problem comes is that we don't know what the __________ success __________ is. They may still feel uncomfortable. Most will go on to use flights again. Some come back for another course."

For those who __________ about changing __________ noises, they may suggest a __________ recording which they can __________ to themselves in a relaxed __________ at home. It may also help to take __________ to the airport to watch planes taking off and __________.

Dr Michael Tarsh, a consultant __________, said: "It is __________ common. There are __________ numbers whose holidays are made horrible for them because of the fear of coming back. Some people are afraid of being in a __________ space. Clearly that is better in a __________ jet. Then there are people who hate turbulence, like me. I don't take alcohol any more on planes because I faint and have to __________ on the floor. Somebody always comes __________ and offers to help, saying they are a doctor. My wife says __________: 'So am I, and so is he'."

But for some people no amount of courses seem __________ to succeed. "I don't believe the thing can stay in the air. I think it's an abomination of nature," was the __________ of one whose feet seem __________ ever to leave the ground."

FURTHER PRACTICE

Hyphenated adjectives

They sit there ***white-knuckled*** (line 13), *a* ***wide-bodied*** *jet* (line 30).
Descriptions like these are very easy to form, but the meanings can be metaphorical. For example, a *cold-blooded* person is cruel and unfeeling. Make *'-ed'* adjectives from these adjectives and nouns and use them to complete the definitions.

cold	hard	small	hand	mind
cool	heavy	soft	head	temper
even	hot	strong	heart	will
faint	kind			

1 If you are ____________ or ____________ you show no sympathy.
2 If you are ____________ you are generous.
3 If you are ____________ you show sympathy and generosity very easily.
4 If you are ____________ you behave fairly.
5 If you are ____________ you behave calmly, especially when under pressure.
6 If you are ____________ you lack courage.
7 If you are ____________ you are sad.
8 If you are ____________ you behave insensitively or with unnecessary force.
9 If you are ____________ you get angry very easily and quickly.
10 If you are ____________ you have a limited view of the world and are rather intolerant.
11 If you are ____________ you behave stubbornly and with determination.
12 If you are ____________ you are determined and have firm opinions.

Idioms with colours

They get into a ***blue funk*** (line 10).
Complete these idiomatic expressions with the appropriate colours, and use them to complete the sentences.

see __________	__________ with rage	once in a __________ moon
in the __________	__________ with envy	through __________-tinted spectacles
in the __________	the __________ rule	__________ in tooth and claw
a __________ area	a __________ opportunity	born with a __________ spoon in her/his mouth

1 It's difficult to see which rules apply to this particular case. It's rather ____________.
2 You really must go to China while you've got the chance. It's ____________.
3 She always looks at life ____________ and never seems to notice that there's crime and poverty all around her.
4 When she accused him of lying he ____________, and left the room ____________.
5 He seldom buys anyone a drink, but ____________ he'll surprise us and pay for a round.
6 At last I've paid off all my debts and I'm ____________ again after being ____________ for about six months.
7 Lucy was ____________ and has never had to worry about money at all.
8 Nature is often described as ____________ because animals kill routinely in order to survive.
9 Everyone was ____________ when they saw her new sports car.
10 ____________ is treat others as you would have them treat you.

20 The problem of laptops on aircraft

VOCABULARY CHECK

Find pairs of words with similar meanings.

anomaly	exclude	incredible	rush very fast
beacon	far-fetched	mounting	signal
circuitry	gadget	peculiarity	stack
device	hurtle	pile	veer
diverge	increasing	rule out	wiring

Word formation

Join items from these lists to form new words. Then use the words to complete the sentences.

in	battery	pit	-controlled
auto	cock	back	-shaped
cone	play	-flight	pilot
remote		-powered	

1 Children like ____________ toys. They are usually ____________ and use radio signals.

2 There are many ____________ services when you travel by air nowadays.

3 The part of an aircraft where the pilot sits is called the ____________.

4 You cannot record with a video ____________ machine.

5 If something is ____________ it is round and pointed.

6 Planes often land on ____________.

COLLOCATION

Noun phrases

How many common noun phrases can you make by combining words from these boxes?

tape	cassette	path	recorder
radio	navigation	player	computer
flight	compact disc	signal	equipment
laptop		beacon	

Adjectives and nouns

Combine these adjectives and nouns to form suitable phrases. Then use the phrases to complete the sentences.

certain	first	striking	amount	example	variety
electronic	mounting	tidal	class	gadget	visibility
in-flight	poor	wide	evidence	movie	wave

1 When you fly, do you ever watch the ____________? Do you travel ____________?

2 You can buy a ____________ of ____________s at the duty-free shop.

3 They blamed ____________ for the crash.

4 This painting is a ____________ of the artist's work when he was at the peak of his powers.

5 There is ____________ that the gap between rich and poor is widening.

6 The fishing village was completely destroyed by a ____________.

Phrases with adverbs

Each word or phrase in the middle box combines well with an item from one of the other boxes. Form phrases, using all the words once only.

land return behave	first firmly strangely particularly to normal heavily safely	concerned published computerized in control

Verb phrases

Use these verbs, in the appropriate form, to complete the sentences.

crash	land	put	sound	veer
emit	lose	set	tune	
hurtle	pick up	shake	turn off	

1 The plane ____________ off course during the storm and ____________ into a mountain.

2 Passengers are not allowed to use portable radios on a plane because they ____________ signals which can be ____________ by the plane's sensitive instruments.

3 They often ____________ planes on automatic pilot nowadays.

4 It ____________ my faith in the company when I saw how disorganised their head office was.

5 He ____________ his life in a most unusual way. I know it ____________ far-fetched, but a piece of an old satellite came ____________ through the air and hit him while he was sunbathing in his garden.

6 This cold weather ____________ the lives of old people at risk.

7 Who ____________ the rules here? Who says we have to ____________ the TV at midnight?

8 I find this radio very difficult to ____________ properly.

VOCABULARY IN CONTEXT

Complete the magazine article, using one of these words or phrases for each space. You will need to change the form of some of the verbs. Use each word or phrase once only.

Nouns	*Adjectives*	*Adverbs*	*Past Participles*	*Verbs*
cassette	certain	enough	diverted	assume
computers	electronic	far	lost	brighten
course	first	firmly	powered	crash
device	forbidden	heavily	pressed	emit
equipment	in-flight	long	published	expand
flight	modern	particularly	ruled	let
gadgets	mounting	regularly	scattered	pick up
interference	normal	safely	shaken	put
laptop	poor	strangely	shaped	set
paperbacks	striking		tuned	sound
player	susceptible			state
series	wide			turn off
stack				veer
tape				
wave				

Hazards aloft

Unless you are born with feathers, flying requires a leap of faith. Passengers have to __________, when they strap themselves in, that a 227,000-kg machine hurtling through the air is __________ in the pilot's control. That faith was __________ last week by a report that a DC-10 coming into New York's Kennedy airport recently almost __________ when a passenger in __________ class turned on his portable compact disc __________.

The story, first __________ in TIME, set off what one airline called "a tidal __________" of concern. Can jets really be __________ from their __________ paths by something as small as a battery-__________ CD player? Or a video-game machine? Or any of a dozen __________ gadgets and computers that passengers __________ carry on board?

Far-fetched as it may __________, it can't be __________ out. Every electrical __________ creates a __________ amount of radiation. Portable phones, remote-control toys and other radio transmitters __________ signals that can carry for kilometers, and their use on planes has __________ been banned. But most airlines still __________ passengers use __________ players, __________ recorders and __________ computers, which make __________ less electromagnetic noise.

Now there is __________ evidence that even these gadgets may be __________ aircraft at risk. A Walkman-type radio __________ to an FM station generates oscillations that can extend 1.5m to 3.7m – far __________, in some planes, to reach the navigation __________ stowed in and around the cockpit. "With their thick wires and vacuum tubes, the old planes probably wouldn't feel a thing," says Bruce Nordwall, avionics editor of *Aviation Weekly & Space Technology*. "But the lowpower circuits in __________ aircraft are much more __________ to interference."

Pilots are __________ concerned about interference with the circuitry that __________ radio signals from the so-called VOR (visual omni-range) network – hundreds of cone-__________ navigation beacons __________ across the U.S. Automatic flight-control systems depend on clear VOR signals to land planes __________ when visibility is __________. But some of that VOR equipment has been behaving __________ of late, occasionally causing aircraft on autopilot to __________ sickeningly out of control.

No planes have crashed and no lives have been __________ – so far. But TIME has obtained a __________ of pilot reports linking a __________ of "anomalies" to a __________ variety of electronic __________, from laptop __________ to Nintendo Game Boys. In one __________ example, a plane flying out of Chicago started veering off __________ while its VOR dials dimmed and danced around. When the passenger in seat 9-D __________ his laptop, the report __________, the "panel lights immediately __________ dramatically and all navigation aids returned to __________."

The U.S. Federal Aviation Administration, __________ by pilots to crack down on the gadgets, issued an advisory late last week that left it up to the airlines to __________ their own rules. Delta has already __________ its list of __________ devices to include video playback machines and CD players. With the arrival of new "fly-by-wire" aircraft, which are __________ computerized and even more vulnerable to __________, passengers may have to go back to reading __________ and watching the __________ movie.

FURTHER PRACTICE

Hyphenated adjectives

Many electronic gadgets are powered by batteries; they are *battery-powered* (line 7). The navigation beacons mentioned in the article (line 22) are shaped like cones; they are *cone-shaped. Far-fetched* (line 10) and *so-called* (line 22) are formed in the same way, using a past participle.

Make hyphenated adjectives containing elements from these lists, in the appropriate form. Then use them to complete the sentences. (Notice that some elements are more common as part of a word than as words themselves, e.g. *oft-* for 'often', and *multi-* for 'many'.)

bare	new
deep	oak
horn	oft
ivy	old
multi	silver
new	snow

cap	fry
cover	lay
face	mow
facet	panel
fashion	repeat
frame	rim

1 You say he's got a(n) ____________ personality. I just think he's a ____________ liar.

2 The tourist brochure was full of ____________ clichés like ' ____________ hay', ' ____________ mountains'.

3 Since he had more money now, he decided to replace his old ____________ glasses with a new ____________ pair.

4 She retired to a(n) ____________ cottage in the country with a(n) ____________, ____________ dining-room.

5 She kept chickens so that she could have ____________ eggs for breakfast.

6 I love ____________ chicken and chips.

Register

Public notices and announcements often use a formal style that is not common in everyday conversation. Make the requests and instructions below more 'official' by using these words, in the apprpriate form, in place of the phrases in italics. Make any other necessary changes.

address	illuminate
alight	proceed
belongings	refrain from
disembark	request
extinguish	smoking material

1 Please *put out* all *cigarettes, cigars and pipes* and *do not* smoke until the no-smoking sign is no longer *lit.*

2 Passengers for Paris are *asked* to *go* to Gate 23.

3 Please take all your *things* with you when you *get off.*

4 Please do not *talk to* the driver.

5 This is not a passenger platform. Do not *get off* here.

21 The phenomenon of mobile phones

VOCABULARY CHECK

Find pairs of words with similar meanings.

ardour	desultory	fashionable	madness	rush	slash	trendy
cut	enthusiasm	frenzy	rise	scramble	soar	unenthusiastic

Use these words to complete the paragraph.

bargain	entrenched	market	niche	promotion
boom	competition	monopoly	operator	slash

When one company is the sole provider of a service or product, that company is said to have a(n) ___________ 1. In that situation it is often difficult for other ___________s2 to get established when the first company is ___________ 3, but if they do, the resulting ___________ 4 is usually good for consumers. Prices are then ___________ed5 and there are special ___________s6 to attract new customers who are on the look-out for ___________s7. It is easier for new producers to enter the ___________ 8 in a ___________ 9 period when everyone has plenty of money to spend. But in a recession, when people are hard up, smaller companies often cannot survive, unless they have found a special section of the market – a ___________ 10 – which they satisfy better than anyone else.

Associations

Find pairs of words or phrases which are associated in some way. They may be similar in meaning, contrasting or complementary.

ardour	monopoly	soar	classrooms
craze	private	prices	mobile
rates	schools	rates	state-owned
numbers	parents	trend	entrenched operator
portable	challenger	kids	competition
lag	digital	frenzy	cellular
leap	fixed-line	analog	catch up

COLLOCATION

Verb phrases

Use these verbs to complete the sentences, changing the form if necessary. Use one verb twice.

chat	dominate	fuel	grab	keep	lap up	slash	step up	transmit

1 I'm not saying she's a gossip, but she does like to ___________ track of what everyone is doing.

2 If you've got a modem you can ___________ computer data by telephone.

3 Large companies are not really interested in ___________ competition, but they will do anything to ___________ a larger share of the market. Ultimately every large company wants to ___________ the market if they can.

4 The shops ____________ prices in the sales and the eager shoppers ____________ the bargains.

5 It's nice to ____________ with friends, and it's so easy to ____________ in touch when you've got a telephone.

6 If wages rise fast it will ____________ an economic boom.

Adjectives and nouns

Use these adjectives to complete the sentences. Use one of them twice.

pricey digital trendy high-flying worldwide

1 He's a ____________ executive who likes to be seen in ____________ restaurants.

2 Some people say mobile phones will soon be as common as ____________ watches, but they're too ____________ for me: the calls are very expensive.

3 It's a ____________ trend: more and more ____________ technology is being used in mobile phone systems.

Noun phrases

Combine these words to form suitable phrases. Then use some of the phrases to complete the sentences.

ski	summer	data	war
car	wireless	share	product
price	computer	house	battery
niche	market	slopes	spectrum

1 He hardly every works. If he's not at his ____________ in the country he's on the ____________ in Switzerland.

2 The company tried to increase its ____________ by popularising their ____________.

3 The ____________ is full of local radio stations nowadays.

4 The ____________ between rival supermarkets has led to certain products being sold very cheaply.

VOCABULARY IN CONTEXT

Complete the magazine article, using one of these words or phrases for each space. You will need to change the form of some of the verbs.

Nouns		*Adjectives*	*Gerunds and Participles*	*Verbs*
ads	race	competitive	lagging	account
battery	sales	digital	lapping up	impress
boom	security	evident	losing	keep
classrooms	share	fixed-line	pushing	keep
data	slopes	high-flying	transmitting	lead
friends	spectrum	private	washing	push
kids	summer	trendy		reach
market	toy			roam
operator	trend			slash
price	war			soar
product	watches			
promotions	world			

Have phone, can travel

The number of cellular-phone subscribers in Western Europe leaped 56% last year, to 23.4 million users, and is sure to keep climbing. Once a pricey __________ for __________ executives, the mobile phone has broken into the personal market. Teenagers chat with their __________, parents use them to __________ track of their __________, and the elderly carry them for an extra measure of __________. The result has been dizzying __________ wars in Britain and phonophilia in Scandinavia, where portable handsets have become nearly as common as digital __________. Danish schools have even found it necessary to ban phones from __________. "This is no longer a niche __________," says Lauri Kivinen, spokesman for Finland's Nokia, which, along with Motorola of the US and Sweden's Ericsson, dominates the hardware __________.

The Euro-craze is part of a worldwide __________. Total global subscribers __________ 57% last year, to 85 million, according to the International Telecommunications Union, and could __________ anywhere from 200 million to 350 million by the year 2000. North America still __________ for about half the __________ market, but Europe, though __________ in subscribers per capita – save in Scandinavia – is fast catching up. Indeed it already __________ the US in the use of __________ technology, which is better at __________ computer __________, harder to eavesdrop on, and can fit more voice channels into the wireless __________ than traditional analog systems.

Stepped-up competition is fueling the __________, as virtually every European country has added at least one new mobile __________ to an industry that typically started out as a monopoly in each nation. Nowhere is this __________ frenzy more __________ than in Britain, where four operators with six networks are deluging newspaper readers and TV viewers with __________ for $15 handsets, free calling time, and other __________ to grab market __________. Consumers are __________ the bargains: the number of British mobile subscribers has doubled in 18 months to 5.8 million. France, normally gadget-happy, is a major laggard in the cell-phone __________, thanks to desultory competition between state-owned France Telecom and __________ rival SFR.

In Italy, just the threat of challenger Omnitel coming on the scene sent entrenched operator Telecom Italia Mobile scrambling to __________ rates. The resulting price __________ has put a *telefonino*, or little telephone, into the hands of 1 in every 6 Italians between the ages of 21 and 60. Italians chat on them in __________ restaurants, on the ski __________, driving motorbikes or just walking down the street. It's a sign you've made it. After the car and the __________ machine, you buy a *telefonino*.

Scandinavia, which pioneered international cell-phone connections in the 1980s, shows no sign of __________ its ardor for mobile phones. In fact, just the opposite: __________ exploded in Norway last summer, __________ subscriber rates to a European-leading 25.3% of the population, and the number of Danish mobiles doubled last year, to about 1 million, serving 18% of the people. Every third person in Stockholm now has a cell phone: Swedes often use portable models as the phones in their __________ houses.

Teenagers are as addicted to going mobile as they are to __________ phones: "If I see a pretty girl at a disco, I like to __________ her by talking on my mobile," says Copenhagen high-schooler Attila Zelikdemir. Even Denmark's vagabonds, who __________ the countryside during the summer, use cell phones to __________ in touch. "My wife didn't like the idea of my being so isolated on the road," says wanderer Sune Olsen. "She calls me up every second day." Recharging? No problem – Olsen carries a car __________ in the pram he __________ along the highways.

FURTHER PRACTICE

-philia / -phobia

Phonophilia (line 5) is an invented word meaning 'a love of telephones', and a person who is very fond of telephones could be called a *phonophile.* Someone who is afraid of telephones could be called a *phonophobe* – someone who suffers from *phonophobia.*

What are these people (1 – 4) particularly fond of, and what fears and loves do words 5 – 12 refer to?

1 bibliophile
2 Anglophile
3 Francophile
4 Europhile
5 linguaphilia
6 technophobia
7 xenophobia
8 photophobia
9 hydrophobia
10 hydrophilia
11 claustrophobia
12 agoraphobia

Advice matching

Here is some advice, from the same article, on how to use a mobile phone. Match these Do's and Don't's with their continuations.

1 Do not say anything on a mobile phone that you wouldn't like to see on the front page of a tabloid newspaper.

2 Do not use a mobile phone in places where people have paid big money to listen to voices other than yours.

3 Do not take a phone into a stuffy British men's club.

4 Do not use one on Paris buses.

5 Do use a mobile if you want the latest in gangster chic.

6 Do not take a cellphone to a job interview.

7 Do remember that how you use your phone reveals a great deal about your character.

A It might ring at the wrong time and convince your prospective boss that you are self-important and insecure.

B The Athenaeum warns its members that all mobile phones must be left with the porter.

C During the kidnapping of German tobacco heir Jan Philipp Reemtsma in Hamburg, the bad guys used a cell phone to direct ransom couriers to the drop-off point.

D When you go out for a pizza with friends, you see there are two kinds of people. Those who turn their *telefonini* off and those who leave them on, put them on the table and hope someone will call.

E An eavesdropper picked up Prince Charles making verbal love to his paramour.

F La Scala opera house in Milan has had so many complaints that Rule No. 9 for ticketholders is, "Leave *telefonini* in the cloakroom."

G Last month passengers watched as a physical therapist who took an important call from a patient was loudly berated by an elderly woman passenger who cried, "Elitism! They can't afford Rolls-Royces, so they ride the bus with portable phones to impress people."

22

"ADVANCED VOCABULARY IN CONTEXT" WATSON (GEORGIAN PRESS) 1997

Do surveillance cameras prevent crime?

VOCABULARY CHECK

Find pairs of words with similar meanings.

assist	drop	identify	limit	rate
civil	equivocal	immense	offence	restrict
crime	example	instance	pinpoint	sensational
debatable	fall	level	public	vast
dramatic	help			

Definitions

Match these words with their definitions. Then use some of the words to complete the sentences, changing the form if necessary.

anecdotal	**a** to work
borough	**b** a discouragement
campaigner	**c** forceful, persuasive
compelling	**d** language that is intended to be persuasive
deterrent	**e** the government ministry dealing with internal affairs
highlight	**f** a town, or an administrative division of a city
Home Office	**g** to emphasise something as important, draw attention to it
ply	**h** based on what people say rather than on facts
rhetoric	**i** a business that lends people money, like a bank, for them to buy a house
building society	**j** someone who takes part in activities in the hope that they will change a particular aspect of society

1 That's a very ____________ argument, but I still don't agree.

2 This report ____________ the needs of working mothers.

3 Fines are not as effective a(n) ____________ against crime as imprisonment.

4 For as long as I've known her she's been a(n) ____________ for prison reform.

5 In *Pygmalion,* Professor Higgins first meets Eliza Doolittle while she is ____________ her trade as a flower-seller.

6 Scientists refuse to accept ____________ evidence. They want hard facts and statistics.

COLLOCATION

Noun phrases

Combine these words to form suitable phrases. Then use the phrases to complete the sentences.

security	radio	centre	staff
vehicle	crime	effect	thefts
building	police	rates	societies
deterrent	city	pagers	investigation

1 There had been so many ____________ in the area that they decided to have a special ____________ into the problem.

2 Doctors sometimes carry ____________ so that they can be contacted easily in case of emergency.

3 Many businesses in the ____________ now have their own ____________ with the result that ____________ have fallen dramatically. Such measures clearly have a ____________.

4 Should I get a mortgage from a bank or from one of the ____________?

More noun phrases

Combine these adjectives and nouns to form suitable phrases. Then use some of the phrases to complete the sentences.

vast	compelling	disorder	majority
public	equivocal	evidence	headlines
limited	sensational	answer	use

1 The Minister gave his interviewer a very ____________ to the question.

2 He agreed that there was ____________ of contamination of the water supply but disapproved of the ____________ in the newspapers, which played on people's fears and could even lead to ____________.

3 He maintained that the ____________ of the population need take no special precautions.

Make three-word phrases by using words from each box.

crime	closed	crime	deterrent	measures	park
strong	overall	circuit	liberties	television	levels
civil	multi-storey	car	prevention	campaigner	effect

Verb phrases

Which verbs can be followed by which nouns? Use some of them to complete the sentences.

commit	express	publish	crime	the guilty	research
convict	identify	reduce	a crime	levels	suspects
deter	install	restrict	criminals	litter	TV cameras
drop	ply	sound	freedom	a note	their trade
	prevent			opinions	

1 People who sell ice cream in the streets should not be given a licence to ____________ their trade unless they also provide waste bins so that their customers don't ____________ litter.

2 They want to ____________ television cameras in the shops in an attempt to ____________ the levels of shoplifting. They hope that the sight of the cameras will ____________ criminals before they actually ____________ a crime.

3 The aim is to ____________ crime without ____________ people's freedom.

4 In ____________ his opinions he said he wanted to ____________ a note of optimism.

VOCABULARY IN CONTEXT

Complete the magazine article, using one of these words for each space. You will need to change the form of some of the verbs. Use each word once only.

Nouns			*Adjectives*	*Verbs*	
answer	evidence	research	civil	act	ply
burglaries	facts	role	clear-cut	commit	prevent
caution	instance	scale	debatable	convict	record
city	instances	staff	deterrent	drop	reduce
claim	levels	stories	guilty	deter	restrict
crime	measures	studies	larger	express	rob
detail	pagers	thefts	limited	identify	sound
drop	parks	thieves	public	install	steal
drops	police	trouble	sensational	lock	watch
			vast	make	

Someone to watch over me

All over Britain, the closed circuit television camera – the spy in the street – is starting to help police with their enquiries. When the Home Secretary opened a CCTV scheme in the Lancashire town of Clitheroe last September he said: "The value of this technology is immense: it __________ crime from happening in the first place, assists __________ investigations, __________ suspects and helps __________ the guilty."

In the decade since the first city-centre CCTVs were __________ , politicians and the police have praised the cameras for their __________ in beating crime. Dramatic __________ in crime rates have made some __________ headlines. But the __________ have been anecdotal. Until last month no systematic __________ on the effectiveness of CCTVs had been published. Now three separate __________ covering the effect of cameras in five different areas have been __________ public – one by the Home Office of CCTV schemes in Birmingham, King's Lynn and Newcastle, and two others of Airdrie in Strathclyde and Sutton in Surrey. For the first time it is possible to look in __________ at the __________ behind the rhetoric.

Undoubtedly the main __________ for CCTVs is that the cameras __________ criminals. But do they prevent crime? The answer is far from __________. Two of the studies found a __________ in crime. But although there was a 13 per cent fall in crimes in the part of Sutton covered by cameras, there was a __________ fall in other parts of the borough because of other crime prevention __________ such as __________ multi-storey car __________ overnight and giving security __________ radio __________.

The Home Office's own research produces a similarly equivocal __________. The research found "compelling __________ " that the cameras "had a strong __________ effect" on crime in Newcastle. However, the report highlights "the failure of the camera system to __________ overall crime __________ within Birmingham __________ centre". CCTVs do not work for all types of crime. __________ and vehicle __________ are offences which the cameras do seem to prevent. But they have less effect on vandalism, assaults and __________ disorder offences.

Richard Thomas, chairman of the Association of Chief Police Officers' committee on security cameras, __________ a note of __________. "There have been cameras in building societies for years and years and we still get people trying to __________ them with nothing covering their faces," he says.

One of the problems common to all __________ prevention schemes is that criminals may simply __________ their trade elsewhere – a phenomenon known as displacement. An obvious __________ of displacement came to light in the Sutton study, where __________ stopped stealing on the streets where they could be caught on camera and started __________ from people in shops instead.

Even if the effect of CCTV on crime prevention is __________, do the cameras help police to arrest criminals and to convict the __________? In King's Lynn the cameras were only of __________ use in pinpointing the criminals. "In the __________ majority of cases when officers requested tape reviews of areas where crimes had been __________, nothing of particular use had been __________ by the cameras," says the Home Office.

The __________ of the introduction of CCTVs has worried __________ liberties campaigners. The organisation Liberty says the cameras can __________ people's freedom to __________ opinions in public. Certainly, you might be forgiven for thinking that Big Brother is __________ you in King's Lynn. The most common use of the cameras there has been to follow people who are __________ suspiciously or who are "known __________-makers". The Home office researchers found about 800 such __________ . No one was arrested. In King's Lynn, the cameras' most frequent success is catching people __________ litter or urinating in public.

FURTHER PRACTICE

Legal vocabulary

Use some of these words to complete the sentences.

accuse	confinement	imprisonment	offender	prosecute
caution	court	jail	penalty	punishment
community	custody	judgement	process	society
compensation	evidence	offence	proof	trial

1 What are the ___________s if an advertiser makes false claims?

2 After a lengthy ___________, he was convicted and sentenced to life ___________.

3 When a young person commits a(n) ___________ for the first time, instead of being sent to ___________, they may be ordered to work in the ___________ or to help their victims by paying them ___________.

4 When a crime is not very serious, the police sometimes give the ___________ a(n) ___________ instead of taking them to ___________.

5 The suspect was arrested and taken into ___________ for questioning.

6 The police were convinced that they had caught the culprit, but they decided not to ___________ because of insufficient ___________.

Connotation

Find pairs of words with similar meanings but different connotations: one of them is usually more positive or more negative than the other. Then complete the sentences with the most appropriate expressions.

be acquitted	fib	impostor	notorious
discreet	fraud	insinuation	reveal
expose	get off scot-free	lenient	secretive
famous	implication	lie	soft

1 a Would you believe it! They found him not guilty. He ___________.
b I'm happy to say the jury found him not guilty. He ___________.

2 a We can afford to be ___________ just this once.
b They accused the judge of being ___________ on drunk driving.

3 a The jury didn't believe her. They could tell she was ___________.
b We told him a(n) ___________ to get him out of the house for a while, so that we could get everything ready for the surprise party.

4 a I disliked his ___________ that she had got the money under false pretences.
b He didn't actually say he would lend us the money, but that was the ___________.

5 a He claims to have healing powers, but he's never healed anyone in his life. He's an absolute ___________.
b He's a(n) ___________. The real Professor Jackson has a birthmark on his left temple.

6 a She blackmailed him by threatening to ___________ him to the police.
b These documents ___________ him to be an honest man.

7 a You can confide in Clara: she's very ___________.
b She's very ___________ about her past. I wonder what she's got to hide.

8 a The British police are ___________ for being unarmed.
b This airport is ___________ for its poor security.

23 Does training help the unemployed?

VOCABULARY CHECK

Match these words with their definitions. Then use some of the words to complete the sentences.

commission	**a** to steal
dole	**b** a set of principles
ethic	**c** more than enough
lavishly	**d** the ability to read and write
literacy	**e** the ability to count and calculate
nominally	**f** to ask someone to do a special piece of work
numeracy	**g** all the people who work in a particular place
poach	**h** the money the government gives to the unemployed
union	**i** in name only, but not in reality
workforce	**j** an organisation that protects the rights and interests of workers and employees

1 Millions of people who are ___________ Christian seldom set foot inside a church.

2 They can't just dismiss you like that. You should complain to your ___________.

3 She's been on the ___________ since she lost her job three months ago.

4 One of the biggest problems facing this country is the decline in ___________ and ___________ among school-leavers.

5 The work ___________ was instilled into him as a child and he feels guilty if he does anything simply for pleasure.

COLLOCATION

Hyphenated adjectives

Join these words to form suitable phrases containing hyphenated adjectives.

well-	search	youths
full-	work	society
post-	trained	education
out-of-	modern	programmes
large-	time	workforce
job-	scale	advice

Adjectives and nouns

Combine these adjectives and nouns to form suitable phrases. Then use some of the phrases to complete the sentences.

high	case
basic	growth
faster	support
strong	education
generous	workforce
productive	unemployment

1 The country owes its economic success and ___________ to the fact that it has one of the most ___________s in the world.

2 We are very grateful for your ___________.

3 The minister made a ___________ for increasing government spending on ___________.

Noun phrases

Combine these words to form suitable phrases. Then use some of the phrases to complete the sentences.

living	intervention
literacy	programmes
skills	standards
training	rates
government	training

1 People who believe strongly in education maintain that those countries with high ____________ will also have higher ____________.

2 Some political parties do not believe in ____________, so they are reluctant to introduce special ____________.

3 Not all employers feel that ____________ is an important priority for their company.

Verb phrases

Combine these verbs and nouns using each one once only. Then use some of the verbs to complete the sentences, changing the form if necessary.

pay	raise	advice	a job
make	release	demand	skills
find	address	a report	the bill
teach	receive	an envelope	years
increase	improve	instructions	a difference
spend	understand	chances	qualifications

1 He can't even ____________ an envelope properly. It would certainly ____________ his chances of ____________ a job if he ____________ his qualifications.

2 They've ____________ a report today about the difference it ____________ if household appliances are supplied with instructions that children can ____________.

3 Children at school should be ____________ more life skills.

4 He's ____________ so much conflicting advice, he doesn't know what to do.

5 He ____________ the last ten years of his life looking after his sick mother.

VOCABULARY IN CONTEXT

Complete the magazine article, using one of these words or phrases for each space. You will need to change the form of some of the verbs. Use each word or phrase once only.

Nouns		*Adjectives, Adverbs and Participles*		*Verbs*	
assistance	piece	devoted	post-modern	address	receive
bottle	place	faster	productive	come off	reduce
case	programmes	full-time	provided	compare	show
demand	qualifications	improved	readily	conclude	spend
economy	rates	less	released	equip	study
education	standards	life-long	skilled	explain	understand
figure	support	lower	strong	find	wonder
help	survey	more	taught	make	work
intervention	wages	out-of-work	widespread	pay	
notice		poached			

Training and jobs: What works?

Many politicians assume that training is one of the best ways to get the jobless off the dole. The evidence suggests that it is not that simple.

On the face of it, the case for generous public __________ for training is __________. Unskilled people are much __________ likely to be out of work than __________ ones; if only their __________ could be improved, they might __________ jobs more __________. Not only would they benefit, but so would the __________ as a whole. A better-trained workforce would be a more __________ one; so more training ought to mean not just __________ unemployment but also __________ growth and higher living __________. Unions like training __________ because they can use them to push up __________. Academics like them because they increase __________ for more education. Parents like them because they give __________, out-of-school youths something to do. Prophets of a __________ society praise them as part of an ethic of __________ learning. And employers don't mind them because the public __________ the bill.

As if all that were not enough, there is even a neat "market failure" argument to __________ why privately __________ training is bound to be inadequate. Why should firms pay to __________ employees with __________ skills when those workers can be __________ at a moment's __________ by competitors? The state must pay, or nobody will. Here, apparently, is a case where government __________ can do some good.

All in all, then, the __________ for publicly supported schemes seems solid. There is just one problem. In practice, they rarely __________.

A notable experiment in America __________ one group of unemployed people who __________ job-search advice with another that got advice plus a __________ on a training scheme. There was no difference in employment or earnings between the two. Another __________ of evidence comes from Sweden, which also __________ lavishly on training the unemployed, and is beginning to __________ whether the policy is worth it. Sweden's parliament commissioned three economists to __________ the country's long-admired "active labour-market programmes", including job search __________, training and relief-work. The authors __________ that while retraining might raise, slightly, the chances of employment, it does so at higher cost, and to __________ effect, than simple job-search advice.

Large-scale training programmes __________ to the uneducated, unskilled and jobless might hope to __________ a big difference – but, as the evidence __________, do not. Often this may be because the skills that matter are more elementary than those __________ in training schemes. If so, the priority should be to improve basic education and so __________ the numbers of hard-to-employ earlier in life. In a report __________ recently, Industry in Education, a British employers' group said that what they really needed was not more skills training but people able to __________ an envelope. An OECD __________ released last year suggested that complaints about basic literacy are __________ even in countries with nominally high literacy __________. In Sweden, which __________ best, one in 12 men could not __________ the instructions on an aspirin __________; in the Netherlands, the __________ was one in ten; in Germany one in seven; and in Canada and America one in five.

There is good cause for providing __________ in basic literacy and numeracy for adults who need it. But do not expect too much. Many of those who have spent ten or more years in __________ education without learning to read or add up may be beyond __________ of this sort.

FURTHER PRACTICE

More vocabulary in context

Complete this further extract from the article on training, using one suitable word in each space. There are several alternatives in some cases.

40 Once in work, on-the-job __________ (as opposed to out-of-a-job training) brings clear improvements
in productivity and wages. That is __________ even for low-wage jobs. A study that followed American
minimum-wage __________ found that after three years of work, only 15% were still working in minimum-
wage __________ – and for many of those, the __________ was a second, part-time one. The rest had
__________ on. For those in __________ , in-house training seems to help mobility.

45 In-house training benefits __________ as well as workers. That is why firms do it. Intel, for example, an
American chip-maker, has a more or less continuous retraining __________ , enabling the firm to
__________ to the volatility of the chip business. Mass-training __________ administered by civil servants
cannot __________ such needs.

The conclusion seems to be that the supposed market failure of training is greatly exaggerated: firms
50 will __________ workers, despite the __________ of poaching, provided that workers are __________ to
meet some of the cost through lower wages, and/or that the __________ concerned are firm-specific
(i.e. not easily sold to another employer). For most workers in most firms, these conditions are met, that is
why __________ training is alive and __________ , without benefit of __________ subsidy.

Where government- __________ training programmes have succeeded they have been either small and
55 focused, concentrating on helping people __________ for work, or else they have equipped people with
basic __________. Arguably, the closer training is to general __________ , the more __________ it is to
succeed. But even if education and training are working as they should, expect no miraculous __________
in unemployment until the costs of labour to __________ , and the benefits of labour to workers, have been
shifted to __________ the market will bear.

Hyphenated adjectives

Certain words such as *long* and *hard* are often used in hyphenated adjectives: *life-long* (line 11), *long-admired* (line 23), *hard-to-employ* (line 30).

Rewrite the sentences below, replacing the words in italics with hyphenated adjectives and making any other necessary changes. Use the elements in the box in the new adjectives. You will need to use two of them twice.

easy long pre new ready short soon

1 Tonight sees the first performance of the composer's tenth symphony, *for which we have been waiting for so long.*

2 She buys a lot of meals *that have been cooked beforehand and are ready for the oven.*

3 After a trial *that lasted three months* he was convicted of fraud.

4 This cupboard, *which is very easy to assemble,* costs less than half the price of the piece of furniture *that is already made.*

5 The couple *are getting married soon* and have been seen everywhere together.

6 *He discovered a new desire* to economise but it *didn't last long at all* and he was soon in debt again. (Begin your sentence 'His ...'.)

The role of futurologists

VOCABULARY CHECK

Use these words to complete the definitions and explanations.

calling	guise	paradigm	state-of-the-art
cool	hot	sequel	throes
corporate	pangs	specificity	workaday
fringe			

1 Something very modern and up-do-date, incorporating the latest ideas, can be described as ___________. If it's popular and sells well, we might say it's ___________.

2 If you are really hungry you are probably feeling the ___________ of hunger.

3 If you really like something, perhaps because it is very fashionable, you might say "That's ___________!"

4 If you are in the ___________ of something, you are in a difficult or painful situation.

5 ___________ is another word for 'exactness'.

6 A book or film which continues the story of a previous one is called a ___________.

7 A job to which you feel particularly dedicated could be called a ___________.

8 To crack down on pickpockets, undercover police officers went about in the ___________ of tourists.

9 If you are on the ___________ of a group you are on the edge, not in the centre of it.

10 The ___________ world is the world of large companies and businesses.

11 The way we currently understand science, and use science to explain the world, is sometimes called the scientific ___________.

12 If something is ___________, it is rather ordinary and uninteresting.

Word formation

Join these words to make new words, and then match them with the definitions.

out	stream
counter	buster
forward-	breaking
ground	looking
block	culture
main	come

a result
b revolutionary
c a very popular book or film
d describes someone who plans for the future
e the life and beliefs of the majority
f the life and beliefs of those who reject the materialistic values of the majority

COLLOCATION

Noun phrases

Combine words from these three boxes to form suitable phrases.

long-	nuclear	list
husband-	scientific	family
traditional	electronics	forecasting
consumer-	and-wife	principles
sound	seller	products
best-	range	team

Combine these words to form suitable phrases to complete the sentences.

21st	computer	radical	analysis	fringe	scientist
atom	death	social	bomb	numbers	throes
birth	environmental	strategic	catastrophe	pangs	war
cold	hard		century	revolution	

1 Since the end of the ____________ the main threat to the world has been the possibility of some ____________.

2 The invention of the ____________ made some people think that humanity would not survive much longer and was even already in its ____________.

3 ____________s still don't fully appreciate how much people have been affected by the ____________.

4 People on the ____________ of the party tried to make a ____________ of how to get more members to adopt their extreme policies.

5 By the 1990s people already started to feel the ____________ of the ____________.

Verb phrases

Combine these verbs and objects. Then use some of the phrases to complete the paragraph, making any necessary changes.

affect	have	a catastrophe	in the press
appear	prevent	credibility	in someone's shadow
bring	set	the outcome	the standard
give	stand	to the masses	a vision

Many science-fiction writers ____________ ____________[1] of Isaac Asimov, who was also a great populariser of science. He really ____________ science ____________[2], and he often ____________ ____________[3] and on television. He ____________ ____________[4] of the future in which robots did all the menial tasks, and he ____________ ____________[5] for all subsequent stories about robots. What ____________ his own stories ____________[6] was that all his robots were programmed with three basic rules which were intended to ____________ a possible ____________[7] in which robots might otherwise have taken over the world.

VOCABULARY IN CONTEXT

Complete the magazine article, using one of these words for each space. You will need to change the form of some of the verbs. Use each word once only.

Nouns		*Adjectives and Adverbs*	*Verbs*	
analysis	pangs	anymore	adapt	give
atom	products	based	affect	imagine
catastrophe	range	cold	appear	invent
cause	revolution	cool	bring	measure
century	sequels	forward-looking	change	occur
creation	specificity	hard	distinguish	prevent
era	team	nuclear	do	set
forecasting	thing	radical	echo	spend
guise	throes	scientific	examine	stand
industry	titles	silly		
kinds	vision	social		
lists	war	wild		

Cashing in on tomorrow

Who will fight the next war in the Middle East? Where will the best new jobs be found next year, and where will the most old ones be lost? What will be the hot consumer-electronics __________ of 2008? How will the Internet change commerce in the 21st __________? Where will the next environmental __________ occur – and what can be done to __________ it?

These are the __________ of questions that are asked – and, for a price, answered – by the __________ folks who call themselves futurists. Once the calling of __________-eyed Cassandras and 19th century writers and __________ scientists on the __________ fringe, long-range __________ has become a sophisticated and quite profitable __________. Its practitioners __________ increasingly in the press and on the best-seller __________. But they all __________ in the shadow of Alvin and Heidi Toffler, the husband-and-wife __________ whose 1970 blockbuster, *Future Shock*, blasted the infant profession into the mainstream and __________ the standard by which all subsequent would-be futurists have been __________.

The Tofflers didn't __________ futurism, of course. H.G. Wells, Jules Verne and George Orwell were all practising futurists working under the science-fiction __________. Fittingly, perhaps, modern futurism was born with the __________ bomb, in that moment when it was suddenly possible to __________ a world without a future. It was Hermann Kahn who __________ the nascent profession credibility with such groundbreaking books as *Thinking About the Unthinkable* (1962), which used sound __________ principles to predict with great __________ the likely effects of a thermonuclear __________.

But it was the Tofflers who __________ futurism to the masses. *Future Shock* made the new profession __________. The book and its best-selling __________, *The Third Wave* (1984) and *Powershift* (1990), __________ not just tomorrow but today, not just one industry but all mankind, making the paradigm-shattering argument that what was really __________ society was the radical acceleration of change itself. Future shock, the Tofflers said, is what happens when change __________ faster than people's ability to __________ to it. The book resonated for the 1960s counterculture, and in some ways it __________ even louder in the digital __________. "People today," says Alvin Toffler, "are scared __________."

That's the great __________ about pondering the future these days: there seems to be so much more of it. Between the computer __________ and the end of the __________ war, between the birth __________ of the international economy and the death __________ of the traditional __________ family, the demand for solid, scientifically __________ forecasting is greater than ever. __________ numbers are difficult to come by, since so much "futurist" work goes on under the guise of economic forecasting or strategic __________, but corporate America clearly has the religion. People who used to have purely planning __________ have been incorporated into other roles. If you're in management at a modern company and you don't __________ at least part of your day thinking like a futurist, you probably aren't __________ your job.

Paul Saffo, who in his decade with the Institute for the Future has consulted for everyone from the U.S. Defense Department to a Swedish on-line service, prefers to __________ between "visionaries" – "people who have a __________ of what the future should be and are trying to make it happen" – and workaday "forecasters" like himself. "My job is to help our clients expand their perceived __________ of possibilities," Saffo says. Of course, in that capacity, he acknowledges, "you can __________ outcomes."

Sometimes, however, it's hard to separate __________ from effect. "Futurism isn't prediction __________," says Douglas Rushkoff. "It's state-of-the-art propaganda. It's future __________."

FURTHER PRACTICE

Figurative expressions

***hot** products, a **cool** profession, the **cold** war, **hard** numbers* (lines 2, 19, 26 and 28).
Sometimes adjectives with quite concrete meanings also have several figurative meanings, especially in informal contexts. Use these adjectives to complete the sentences.

cold	cool	lukewarm	warm	hot	hard	soft

1 Don't take any notice of what he says; it's just a lot of ____________ air.

2 She's always had a ____________ spot for her youngest son.

3 There are no ____________ and fast rules. You just have to use your common sense.

4 The Minister refused to be interviewed on the scandal affecting his colleague. The topic is just too ____________ to handle.

5 The film left me ____________; I just couldn't get interested in it.

6 No one was very keen on her ideas, and they got a rather ____________ response.

7 There was a power struggle between the moderate wing of the party and the ____________ right.

8 It was a lovely evening. They gave us a really ____________ welcome.

9 I can't leave work early. My boss is very ____________ on time-keeping.

10 He decided to play it ____________ and wait for someone else to make the first move.

11 The bank robbers drove off with the police in ____________ pursuit.

12 He thought she would be a ____________ touch and was really surprised when, even after listening to his ____________ -luck story, she refused to lend him any money.

13 I didn't like him much at first, but I soon ____________ed to him.

14 I'm afraid my Italian is not so ____________.

Compound adjectives

***groundbreaking** books* (line 16), a ***paradigm-shattering** argument* (line 20).
Use these words to complete the sentences. Form adjectives where necessary with nouns plus present participles. Notice that these expressions are mostly figurative in meaning.

blow	break	take	breath	heart
boggle	shatter	warm	earth	mind

1 A: It ____________ the ____________ to think how much that ugly building cost.
B: You're right. It's absolutely ____________ – ____________.

2 A: It ____________ my ____________ to see how genuinely friendly and helpful the children were to the blind boy.
B: I agree. It was a(n) ____________ sight.

3 A: When I looked down from the top of the tower it ____________ my ____________ away.
B: Yes. The view was simply ____________.

4 A: It ____________ my ____________ to see how cruelly the animals are treated.
B: You're right. It's truly ____________.

5 A: When we saw that science-fiction film for the first time it simply ____________ our ____________; there had never been anything like it before.
B: That's true. It was a(n) ____________ – ____________ experience.

6 If it could be proved that we do have a sixth sense, it would be a(n) ____________ – ____________ discovery.

Review 4 (Units 19 - 24)

Complete these sentences with the most appropriate words from units 19 to 24. Sometimes the initial or final letters are given to help you.

UNIT 19

1 The two jumbo jets narrowly missed being involved in a ______ - ______ __________**n**.

2 It was a very popular exhibition. There were **v**__________ **n**__________ of people queuing to get in on the first day.

3 She was often afraid of the dark as a child, and even now often has a **p**__________ __________ if the lights suddenly go out.

4 There are various **r**__________ **t**__________ you can try if you suffer from stress. There's massage, yoga, breathing and even self-hypnosis, to name just a few.

5 She suffered from arachnophobia and went to a hypnotist to see if he could help her **c**__________ her __________ of spiders.

6 He'd been waiting for years for the chance to go to Hollywood. This film was a **g**__________ **o**__________ for him to make his name in America.

7 This case isn't really covered by the law as it stands. It's rather a __________**y** **a**__________.

8 He's always very **c**__________ – __________**ed** in a crisis and never panics.

9 She says honesty is always the best policy. That's her __________**n** **r**__________.

10 He's a very **e**__________ – __________**ed** interviewer and in discussion programmes he always makes sure everyone has their fair share of air-time.

UNIT 20

1 They've changed the __________ __________ so that planes don't fly so close to residential areas.

2 I was going to finish writing the report on the train, but it was on disk, and although I had my __________**p** __________ with me I'd forgotten to check that the battery was charged.

3 Some politicians say there is **m**__________**ing** __________ that crime and deprivation are related, but the Prime Minister says the statistics are misleading.

4 They sell a __________**e** __________**y** of fruit and vegetables from all parts of the world.

5 The plane was unable to land at Heathrow owing to __________**r** __________**y** and was diverted to Manchester.

6 We've got an **e**__________ **g**__________ in our car that tells us when someone has forgotten to fasten their seat-belt.

7 The passenger plane was shot down by mistake when it **v**__________ off __________ and crossed into enemy air-space.

8 It **s**__________ your __________ in human nature when you hear how cruelly people sometimes take advantage of each other.

9 I know it __________ __________**ed** but I haven't made it up. It's absolutely true.

10 Storing things in front of fire escape doors and keeping them locked __________ people's lives at __________.

UNIT 21

1 When you're walking around a supermarket, putting things in your basket, it's hard to __________ __________ of how much you're spending.

2 She promised to __________ in __________ when she moved to Scotland, but we haven't heard from her for six months now.

3 The economic __________**m** was __________**ed** by the rapid rise in house prices and the increase in borrowing. People had more money to spend than ever before.

4 You need a modem if you want to **t**__________ computer __________ by telephone.

5 They're typical yuppies, always going to wine bars and having dinner in __________**y** __________**s**.

6 Their profits were down this year because of the __________ __________ they waged with their rivals during which they sold things far too cheaply.

7 He joined the rat-race, became a **h**_____ – _____**ing** __________**e** in an international company before he was thirty, and died of a heart-attack at 45.

8 IBM was one of the biggest computer companies and **d**__________**ed** the __________ for a long time, selling more computers than any other manufacturer.

9 Far fewer people read the quality press than read **t**__________ __________**s**.

10 It's always difficult to know what to wear when you go to a __________ __________. Do you dress normally, or do you dress to impress your prospective boss?

UNIT 22

1 You must admit, when you hear about such tragedies it's a **c**_________ **a**_________ against allowing people to drink and drive.

2 One of the main arguments in favour of capital punishment is its supposed **d**_________ **e**_________. According to this view, criminals are less likely to kill if they think they may in turn be killed when they are caught.

3 Many people believe that corporal punishment is an _________ _________ against bad behaviour in school.

4 Scientists generally rule out the possibility of telepathy because there are no hard facts to support it, only **a**_________ **e**_________.

5 Some people never trust statistics. When _________ **r**_________ go down they say it's because people aren't reporting robberies and burglaries because they know the police can't do much about them.

6 The **v**_________ _________ of the population are honest, law-abiding citizens.

7 When challenged by journalists, the manager of the nuclear power station gave an _________ _________**r**, neither confirming nor denying the rumours that there had been a radiation leak.

8 People who own guns say it would be an infringement of our **c**_________ **l**_________**s** to outlaw private gun ownership.

9 To what extent does the obligation to carry identity cards _________ our personal _________**m**?

10 She **s**_________**ed** a **n**_________ of warning in her speech, saying that we should not expect the situation to improve overnight.

UNIT 23

1 This concert would have been impossible without the _________**s** **s**_________ of our sponsors, the North Western Banking Group.

2 In his address to the meeting he made a **s**_________ **c**_________ for changing the rules, but in the end the committee decided to stay with the status quo.

3 It isn't special training that these job-seekers need but **b**_________ **e**_________.

4 They will soon have one of the most educated populations in the region: there are more children in _____–_____ _________ today than at any time in the country's history.

5 If a country is to have a _____–**t**_____ **w**_________ it should encourage employers to provide in-house training for their employees.

6 Some political parties try to adopt a laissez-faire approach to everything and disapprove of **g**_________ **i**_________.

7 It's true that wages have increased, but so have prices, and general **l**_________ _________**s** haven't actually changed much at all over the last ten years.

8 It _________ no _________ whether you want to do it or not. You have no choice. You've got to.

9 He was brought up with a strong _________ **e**_________ and as he grew older he became something of a workaholic, unable to enjoy the simple pleasures of life.

10 They say we are living in a _____–_____ _________**y**, perhaps because our parents and grandparents already described their own period as 'modern'. So what will come next? How will our children and grandchildren refer to their times?

UNIT 24

1 On an expedition you just have to learn to ignore the _________**s** of _________ when your food supplies are getting low.

2 Even though political commentators had been saying for years that communism in Europe was in its **d**_________ _________**s**, it still came as a surprise when so many regimes toppled almost overnight.

3 Some people date the end of the _________ **w**_________ from the fall of the Berlin Wall in 1989.

4 He has always been on the **r**_________ **f**_________ of the party. His views are far too extreme for me.

5 A hundred years ago people had much closer relationships with their grandparents, aunts and uncles, but now even the **n**_________ _________**y** seems to be in danger of breaking down.

6 The political leaders said that the recent terrorist explosion would not **a**_________ the **o**_________ of the ongoing peace talks, which were nearing their conclusion.

7 The pianist said she owed her success to the fact that she had trained under a very demanding teacher, who always **s**_________ very high _________**s** of performance.

8 It doesn't matter if you miss her speech. She's full of _________ **a**_________ and never really says anything.

9 They gave me a very **w**_________ _________**e** when I arrived and made me feel really at home.

10 We had _________**ing** _________**s** of the islands from the helicopter

Key

Unit 1

1 invest 2 fraud 3 watchdog 4 broker
5 jargon 6 squad 7 shares 8 debtor
9 stock market 10 yuppie 11 partners
12 deal

Pairs

tumble/fall, reveal/show, offence/crime, numerous/many, glean/pick up, fully-fledged/mature, collapse/fall, claim/demand, audacious/daring

Noun phrases

1 economics lesson, lunch break
2 telephone order 3 Stock Exchange jargon
4 fraud squad 5 share ownership

Adjectives and nouns

1 senior partner 2 individual case
3 certain amount 4 Bad debts 5 tumbling prices 6 latest jargon 7 naughty boy
8 big losers, estimated losses

Verb phrases

1 costs money 2 buy shares 3 open an account 4 place an order 5 meet your debts
6 damage your case

Boy invested £100,000 during school breaks

The Stock Market collapse claimed another victim yesterday when a *big* loser was *revealed* to be a boy, aged 15, who *slipped* home from school during lunch breaks to place telephone *orders* for £100,000 *worth* of shares with his brokers.

The schoolboy successfully passed himself off to brokers as a fully-fledged *yuppie* businessman, aged 19, by using the latest Stock Exchange *jargon* gleaned from *economics* lessons at his school in Derbyshire.

But the *audacious* dealings of the *unnamed* schoolboy came uncomfortably to light when *tumbling* Stock Exchange prices left the numerous brokers who bought *shares* in companies on his *behalf* with *estimated* losses of £20,000 that he could not *meet*.

Mr Michael Somerset-Leek, *senior* partner in Coni, Gilbert and Sankey, stockbrokers, one of the *firms* used by the schoolboy, said yesterday: "Obviously he has been very *naughty*. He *dealt* through our Wolverhampton office and has *cost* us some money, but anything I say may *damage* our case in *claiming* money from the lad."

Mr Somerset-Leek said that when a new customer *opened* an account "there has to be a *certain* amount of good will on both *sides*".

"It is just one of the problems of wider share *ownership*," he added.

When the schoolboy started *buying* shares his name was apparently cleared by the Stock Exchange Mutual Reference Society, an internal *watchdog* that checks for bad *debtors*.

Now the schoolboy is being *interviewed* about "possible *offences*" by *fraud* squad detectives in Derbyshire. His headmaster said yesterday: "I am *aware* of this boy's case, but it is not something I want to *talk* about. "All I can *say* is that he *told* me he went home at lunch-time and ordered shares there."

The Stock Exchange yesterday said it could not *comment* on an *individual* case.

Craig Seton in *The Times*

Register

1c 2b 3c 4n 5m 6o 7e 8a 9f
10m 11j 12k 13d 14l 15g 16g
17h 18i 19q 20p

Sentence adverbs

sadly d, foolishly c, undoubtedly g, unexpectedly f, naturally h, frankly a, personally b, luckily e

1 Personally/Frankly 2 Foolishly 3 Sadly
4 Naturally 5 undoubtedly 6 Luckily
7 unexpectedly 8 Frankly/Personally

Unit 2

craze d, braille c, brainwave b, copyright g, royalty f, mature e, bug a

1 copyright, royalty 2 bug 3 craze
4 mature 5 braille 6 brainwave

Noun phrases

1 world championship, front page
2 department store, electronic version, board game 3 crucial decision, home town
4 five-cent royalty, marketing agent
5 varying sizes

Verb phrases

1 take 5 years 2 earn royalties 3 score points, master the game 4 hit on an idea, team up with someone 5 think up a new name 6 catch the bug 7 show no signs of

Common expressions

long dead, right first time, according to experts, desperate for money, the number of points, each letter of the alphabet, at the peak of sales

Poor-spelling SCRABBLE inventor dies

The man who invented the word game Scrabble because he was *desperate* for money during the Great Depression has died, aged 93.

By the time Alfred Mosher Butts died in hospital in his *home* town of Rhinebeck, New York, *sales* of the game had *passed* 100 million and it had its own world *championship*. But the 1931 brainwave *took* 20 years to mature after Butts began by making the game in his garage and selling it to neighbours and anyone he could *interest*.

Scrabble showed no *signs* of becoming a bestseller until the owner of Macy's *department* store in New York caught the *bug* while on holiday in 1952. Within a year it was a *national* craze.

However, Butts always said that Scrabble had never made him rich. By the time it had become a world *bestseller*, he earned only a five-cent *royalty* on each set *sold*, a deal which gave him about $50,000 a year at the *peak* of sales in the fifties and sixties. His copyright *expired* in 1974, and the income *dried up*. He lived comfortably *enough*, however, from his work as an architect.

Butts first *called* his game Criss-Cross, and then Lexico. It became Scrabble in 1948, when Mr Butts *teamed up* with a marketing agent, James Brunot. But who *thought up* the familiar name is lost to history; Brunot is *long* dead, and Butts recently said he could not remember who had *hit on* Scrabble.

Butts never *mastered* the game which combined his *liking* for jigsaws and crosswords with his professional sense of pattern and space.

"When I played him, he *confessed* that he was not a very good speller, and I beat him," said Mr John Williams, president of the National Scrabble Association. "He was a *wonderful* man, really a classic American genius."

Butts, according to *experts*, was most remarkable for getting the game right *first* time. The *crucial* decisions on the number of each letter of the *alphabet* in each set and the number of points *scored* when they are used to make words have never been changed, except to conform with the frequency of *use* in languages *other* than English.

Butts decided on the value of the letters by *examining* the number of times they were used on a *single* front page of *The New York Times*.

The game is now *available* in *varying* sizes and comes either as a *conventional* board game or in an electronic *version*. Translations *include* French, Spanish, Hebrew and Russian, and there is a Braille version.

Charles Laurence in *The Daily Telegraph*

Vocabulary

1 mature 2 bug 3 mastered 4 genius, master 5 bugged

Expressions with *idea*

1 put, f 2 good, g 3 bright, e 4 toying, c 5 odd, i 6 faintest, a 7 hit, h 8 very, d 9 whole, b

Collocation and idiom

1 rich vocabulary (poor) 2 poor at (good) 3 richly deserved (not) 4 poor health (good) 5 rich colours (pale/dull) 6 rich soil (poor) 7 rich in (lacking in/deficient in/poor in) 8 poor quality (good/high) 9 riches (poverty) 10 poor pay (good/high) 11 rich food (plain/bland) 12 poorly (well)

Unit 3

Similar meanings: site - place, mania - craze, plush - luxurious/opulent, plaque - plate, tinker - play about, burgeon - develop rapidly, genesis - origins, hierarchy - order according to rank, degree - university qualification

Opposites: scorn - admire, shabby - well-maintained, austere - luxurious/opulent

1 tinkering 2 site 3 burgeoning, 4 plush, mania, scorned, austere

Adjectives and nouns

1 classical music 2 bronze plaque 3 informal style 4 strict hierarchy 5 senior executive, personal fortune, new invention

Electronic or *electronics*?

electronic calculator/equipment/instruments
electronics company/engineer/industry

Noun phrases

birthplace (*one word*), drawing board, industrial site, leafy street, office corridors, opulent house, plush office, shop floor

Verb phrases

1 toss a coin 2 form a partnership 3 make a living 4 go public 5 take advantage 6 subscribe to the view (*Not used:* own a site, lose your job, put up a building)

Computer giant in a garage

The monument to David Packard, the electronics engineer, is a bronze *plaque* on the lawn of a pleasant but not opulent house in a *leafy* street in Palo Alto, California. The house was not his birthplace, but its small and *shabby* wooden garage is regarded as the genesis of Silicon Valley and the computer industry.

It was here, in the 12-by-18ft building *put up* in 1905, that Packard and his friend Bill Hewlett began in the autumn of 1938 to *tinker* with their new *invention*, an electronic audio oscillator that Walt Disney later used to test sound *equipment* for his classical music cartoon, Fantasia. So powerful was the legend of Hewlett-Packard's origins that today in the computer industry a failure is *met* not with "back to the drawing *board*" but "back to the garage".

Packard, co-founder of the huge Hewlett-Packard electronics company, also invented a management *style* known as the "HP Way" that is still *practised*. It is *informal* but efficient, and includes such concepts as "management by walking around", in which executives roam the shop *floor* and office *corridors* meeting employees and seeking their ideas.

Packard was *born* the son of a successful lawyer and high-school teacher in the town of Pueblo, Colorado and, despite the family's *wishes* for a law career, he *obtained* a master's *degree* in electrical engineering at Stanford. He *studied* under Professor Frederick Terman, who was concerned that so many of his brightest graduates went "back east" to *make* their living. The professor, now *regarded* as the father of the US electronics industry, wanted them to *form* their own companies on an industrial *site* the university owned. Packard and his fellow student Hewlett were among the first to *take* advantage of the offer.

They formed their partnership on New Year's Day 1939 with just $538 in *capital* ,and *tossed* a coin to decide in what order to put their names. "We weren't interested in making money," Packard *recalled* later, "but if you couldn't get a job, you made one for yourself. Our first several years we made only 25 cents an hour."

However, in the first year they had a *profit* of $1,539 on sales of "inventions to order" of $5,369. Their company became a *leading* supplier of *electronic* instruments and equipment that *eventually* led the partners into the burgeoning *field* of computers. They built their first model, the HP-2116a, in 1966, but made more money on the *popular* electronic calculator they introduced in the early 1970s.

Today Hewlett-Packard is the second largest *computer* company in the United States, with sales of $31.5 billion *annually* and 100,000 employees. Forbes magazine estimated Packard's *personal* fortune at $3.7 billion, but he lived *austerely* and did not subscribe to the *current* "downsizing" mania in which hundreds of thousands of Americans from lathe operators to senior *executives* have lost their jobs.

Packard wrote down his management beliefs when the company *went* public in 1957. It scorns a strict *hierarchy* but encourages individual creativity while urging a "company culture" of respect and trust. Packard believed in dispersing power and would *split up* divisions after they reached 1,500 employees. Executives at HP had no limousines or private dining-rooms and Packard did away with *plush* offices, installing cubicles without doors instead, while encouraging engineers to leave their work out so others could come by and tinker or *offer* ideas.

Christopher Reed in *The Guardian*

Inventor vocabulary

1 designer 2 discoverer 3 architect
4 pioneer 5 architect 6 creator 7 author
8 founder 9 instigator 10 originator
11 author 12 inventor 13 father

More collocations and vocabulary

1 split up/break up/go their separate ways
2 formal style, loose hierarchy
3 spartan/austere/bare/primitive offices
4 demolished/pulled down those buildings
5 disagrees (with it)/opposes it/takes the opposite view 6 residential area
7 hovel/shack 8 junior executive

Unit 4

1 foster/encourage 2 weakness/frailty, bout/period 3 angst/anxiety/anguish
4 stress/tension 5 connection/link/ties
6 pursue/follow 7 ponder/consider
8 trigger/spark

Adjectives and nouns

1 inner tension 2 physical frailty 3 mental illness 4 budding genius, outstanding individuals, general population 5 creative arts
6 final analysis, emotional factors
(*Not used:* statistical rigour)

Noun phrases

a bout of illness, a blend of chemicals, a period of life, a feeling of inferiority, a variety of factors, a member of a profession, the top of the ladder

Common phrases

1 searching for clues 2 sit on the throne
3 Contrary to expectations 4 the secret of success 5 bridge the gap 6 outline the findings 7 as distinct from 8 clues to genius 9 emotionally draining
10 permanently damaged

Mapping your way out of mediocrity

For thousands of years, philosophers have pondered the ties between madness and creativity. Now this *link* has been examined with statistical *rigour* by Professor Arnold Ludwig of Kentucky University, who outlines his *findings* in a new book.

Instead of leafing through medical notes searching for *clues* to genius, Prof Ludwig *relied* on biographies of 20th-century people reviewed in *The New York Times* from 1960 to 1990. In this way he gathered the names of 1004 poets, journalists, artists and business *leaders*. He analysed the extent of mental *illness* in each field, examined other *emotional* factors fostering greatness, then created a so-called template for success.

Prof Ludwig believes genius requires a precise *blend* of brain chemicals (inherited) and environmental cues. Not surprisingly, he finds that "members of the artistic *professions* or *creative* arts suffer more types of mental difficulties and do so over longer *periods* of their lives than members of other professions."

Prof Ludwig finds that 24 per cent of his sample had suffered the death of a parent before the age of 14. A previous *study* of 24 British prime ministers found that 63 per cent had suffered the *loss* of a parent by the age of 15. The rate in the *general* population is 17 per cent.

"*Contrary* to conventional expectations, not all people are permanently devastated or *damaged* by such a loss," Prof Ludwig writes.

Some 10 per cent of his *sample* suffer genetic disability and another 10 per cent have suffered illness for at least six months during their youth. Prof Ludwig *speculates* that physical *frailty*, like the death of a parent, sparks an inner *angst*, a feeling of inferiority, that drives children to excel.

The *crucial* clues to genius, the heart of Prof Ludwig's argument, are revealed in his *final* analysis, in which he *subdivides* his sample to distinguish thinkers such as Albert Einstein or even Agatha Christie from élite such as kings. ("All they did was sit on the throne," Prof Ludwig says.)

Outstanding individuals tend to be born with talent, have creative parents, a mentally *ill* mother, a tense household and a *bout* of *physical* illness. Above all else, Prof Ludwig highlights "psychological unease", as *distinct* from mental illness.

"This is *extremely* important because *unlike* past studies that have talked about mental illness, I talk about the sense of unease that *bridges* the gap between those who are motivated and driven and those who are normal psychologically but who have the capacity to *generate* inner tension," Prof Ludwig says. This inner tension – whether *triggered* by a psychiatric illness or by the death of a loved one – encourages the *budding* genius to bury himself in his work sometimes at the expense of his happiness. Prof Ludwig believes true psychological unease is the result of a *variety* of factors.

Now that we all have the secret of success, the real question is whether we want to *pursue* it. Do we want to endure chronic *inner* tension to reach the top of the *career* ladder? Do we want to bring up children who are *burdened* by mental anguish? Not even the best psychiatrist can predict the path best for you, the merry stroll of mediocrity or the *emotionally* draining ascent of success. And that, says Prof Ludwig, is why he called his book *The Price of Greatness*.

Randi Epstein in *The Daily Telegraph*

Negative prefixes

1 indistinct 2 disinherited 3 unconventional 4 abnormal 5 uneasy 6 discomfort 7 unable 8 disconnected 9 unmotivated 10 unburdened 11 disability 12 unconnected

Misleading 'negatives'

1 uncouth 2 indelible 3 inept 4 inflammatory 5 incorrigible 6 infamous 7 innocuous 8 dismay 9 inflammable 10 insidious 11 ungainly 12 unkempt

Unit 5

1b (a = *drought*) 2a (b = *snips*) 3b 4a 5a 6a 7b 8b (a *rabble* is a noisy crowd) 9a (b = *incontrovertible*) 10b (a = *riot*) 11a (b = *megalomaniac*) 12a 13a

Adjectives and nouns

1 future prospects 2 research purposes
3 general public 4 academic circles
5 historical finds, vast cave, clear picture
(*Not used:* burning torch)

Noun phrases

1 galleries, stones 2 the century, *Homo sapiens* 3 mystery, globe

More noun phrases

1 a draught of warm air 2 Groups of human colonists 3 The level of artistic ability
4 The evolution of man's mind, the greatest of scientific mysteries

Adverbs with adjectives and participles

largely oblivious, d previously unsuspected, a roughly the same, c unprecedentedly clear, e widely dispersed, b

Re-ordering

1 the world's oldest known paintings
2 the three main rival explanations
3 an unsuspected global environmental event
4 the most spectacular intellectual step

The oldest masters of all

On 18 December 1994, three French cavers were exploring a canyon in southern France when they felt a *draught* of warm air coming from a *pile* of stones. They removed the rubble, and uncovered a *vast* cave that had been *sealed* off from the *outside* world for hundreds of centuries. Inside, they found themselves face to face with more than 200 cave paintings of animals that once *roamed* Europe: rhinos, lions, bears and bison – stunning portraits now *verified* as the world's *oldest* known paintings.

Academic *circles* have been *thrown* into turmoil by the discovery of what is now *known* (after one of the cavers who found it) as the Chauvet cave. Most of the rest of the world remains largely *oblivious* to the excitement. Apart from a few initial snaps in the press, there has been little *opportunity* for the *general* public to admire the paintings, the cave itself having been sealed for research *purposes*.

Preliminary research *suggests* that the 35,000-year-old drawings were *partly* religious in nature. The cave, in the Ardèche, in south-east France, was never *lived* in by humans. Rather, it was a pitch-dark hidden *network* of galleries, some of them 30m high and 70m long; the Stone Age artists would have required *burning* torches to *illuminate* it.

The drawings show a level of *artistic* ability *previously* unsuspected for the period. Each masterpiece features perspective, shadow – even movement. But the Chauvet cave is far more than *simply* the art *find* of the decade. It may also offer *clues* to one of the greatest of all scientific mysteries: the *evolution* of man's creative mind.

Homo sapiens evolved in Africa some 150,000 years ago and *dispersed* around the world about 100,000 years ago. However, there is no *evidence* of art having existed until around 40,000 years ago. Then, over the following 12,000 years, in Australia, Europe and southern Africa, there seems to have been an as yet *inexplicable* intellectual revolution in which art was produced. Scientists have long been *baffled* as to how creative thought developed almost *simultaneously* in three such *separate* areas of the globe. Clues in the Chauvet cave – footprints, handprints, bones – may, by offering an unprecedentedly *clear* picture of prehistoric ritual, help to *explain* how and why humanity in this period *suddenly* became able to *engage* in symbolic thought.

There are three main *rival* explanations. First, there could have been an as yet *undetected* global environmental event which *triggered* the rapid simultaneous development of creative thought. Second, it could be that, after spreading out from Africa, the *widely* dispersed *groups* of human colonists each progressed culturally at *roughly* the same speed, despite different environments. Or, most *controversially* of all, it could be that the human brain continued to *evolve* – rapidly, in evolutionary terms – after the emergence of *Homo sapiens*.

If this last theory is correct, the *implications* for evolutionary and psychological thinking, not to *mention* humanity's *future* prospects, might be considerable. The paintings are spectacular – but the cave's interest is that, in the words of Jean Clottes, senior archaeologist at the site, "Our research will help us to understand what the Stone Age artists were doing in the cave." Let us *hope* that it does: for the revolution in human thought which the paintings *represent* was perhaps the most *significant* intellectual step ever taken by mankind.

David Keys in *The Independent on Sunday*

Time expressions

1 historic, era 2 turn, century 3 millennia (*the plural of* millennium) 4 eons, Age 5 decades 6 historical 7 prehistory, historical 8 fraction, second 9 hour 10 history, historic 11 century, period, history 12 light years

Words with *-spect*

1 prospecting 2 In retrospect 3 respect 4 introspective 5 made a spectacle of 6 prospective, inspected 7 perspective on 8 aspect

Unit 6

1a 2b 3a 4b 5b 6b 7b 8b 9a (b = *overtake*) 10b (a = *fast lane*)

Hyphenated words

1 double-quick 2 under-perform 3 long-term 4 fast-tracking 5 non-threatening 6 left-hand

Verb phrases

1 achieve 2 acquire 3 suggest 4 employ 5 improve 6 quicken 7 work

Lexical sets

knowlege/skills, language/number, liver/lungs, panic/stress, parts/overview, picture/diagram, song/poem, test/exam

1 neurological, psychological 2 pleasant, non-threatening 3 musical, auditory, visual 4 bright, with learning difficulties 5 whole, constituent

Adverbs

1 dramatically 2 particularly 3 widely 4 commonly 5 seriously

How to be smarter with the same brain

We've all seen the adverts. Improve your IQ, learn a language in *double-quick* time – it's as simple as ABC. But can you really *become* smarter or *learn* more quickly with the same brain? And if you can, why don't schools *employ* the same techniques?

The fact is that more and more schools are using accelerated learning approaches because the techniques can *dramatically* improve learning *capability*, based as they are on neurological and psychological *research* into how the brain *works*, how it *acquires* new knowledge, understanding and skills and how it *recalls* what it has learned.

Accelerated learning draws together the work of psychologists and *educationists* around the world, most of whom *start* from the frightening conviction that almost all children in school, from the brightest to those with learning *difficulties*, seriously under-perform.

American research *suggests* that early intensive education can improve IQ *scores* by up to 30 points. Accelerated learning does not mean fast-tracking very bright pupils. It is an *approach* to learning that quickens the *pace* and absorption of learning for all abilities. Accelerated learning *methods* are not difficult or *expensive* and can be used in any classroom.

The *human* brain is segmented. There is a *section* concerned with survival, which can override everything else if it is stimulated and another concerned with emotion. If you panic, or are under *stress*, you do not have any capacity to learn at the same time. So accelerated learning techniques put a lot of *emphasis* on creating a pleasant, *non-threatening* environment for students.

Another part of the brain deals with long-term memory. If learning is to *last* longer than the next test or *exam*, it has to be *transferred* to the long-term memory. *Visual* and musical clues can help. Many people find it easier to recall a song or a *poem*, a picture or a *diagram* than a chunk of prose.

Another two segments of the brain, *commonly* known as the left-hand and right-hand brain, deal with the mechanics of learning. The left deals with language, mathematics, logic and linearity and it tends to learn bottom up. In other words, if it were learning about the human *body* in biology it would prefer to start with the *constituent* parts, like the lungs and the liver and build up to the *whole* organism. Meanwhile the right-hand brain deals with spatial *concepts*, music, images, imagination. It prefers to learn by moving from the *overview* to the constituent parts.

According to Professor Howard Gardner, of Harvard University, there are three ways of learning – the visual, the auditory and the kinaesthetic (concerned with touch and action) – and you *achieve* your *maximum* potential by using all three. *Sesame Street*, the television *programme* for pre-schoolers, used a brilliant mix of the visual and the *auditory* in cartoons and sketches, to teach basic *language* and number.

Traditionally, particularly in *secondary* schools, the emphasis has been on listening, reading and making *notes*. But in an average *class*, many children will be *seriously* disadvantaged if their *preferred* visual and kinaesthetic approach is ignored.

Accelerated learning *projects* have been tried out extensively in the United States, New Zealand and some European countries. Accelerated methods for learning languages have been *particularly* successful and are *widely* used in industry and in universities. Increasingly schools in the UK are finding that they, too, can learn from the accelerated approach.

Maureen O'Connor in *The Independent*

Matching

1D 2C 3B 4A 5F 6E

Verbs with *-en* and *en-*

1 loosens 2 enrages 3 tighten
4 endangers 5 entitled 6 fattening
7 entrap 8 enlarged 9 slackens 10 enrich
11 enslaved 12 lengthened

Review 1

UNIT 1

1 certain amount
2 individual case
3 lunch break
4 naughty boy
5 bad debts
6 fraud squad
7 commit the crime
8 open an account
9 place the order
10 come to light

UNIT 2

1 latest craze
2 travel bug
3 front page
4 crucial decision
5 hit on the idea
6 faintest (*or* slightest) idea
7 According to experts
8 richly deserved
9 poor health
10 showing signs

UNIT 3

1 building site
2 classical music
3 strict hierarchy
4 senior executives
5 fashion designer
6 tosses a coin
7 make a living
8 form a partnership
9 subscribe to the view
10 drawing board

UNIT 4

1 budding genius
2 general population
3 creative arts
4 final analysis
5 bout of illness
6 searching for clues
7 bridge the gap
8 contrary to expectations
9 uneasy feeling
10 incorrigible liar

UNIT 5

1 future prospects
2 general public
3 clear picture
4 clue to this mystery
5 almost the same

6 historic moment
7 academic circles
8 thrown into turmoil
9 artistic ability
10 research purposes

UNIT 6

1 long-term plans
2 quicken the pace
3 acquire knowledge
4 achieve ... potential
5 improved dramatically
6 commonly known
7 seriously disadvantaged
8 tighten my belt
9 attention span
10 abstract concepts

Unit 7

fuel d, germ f, dwarf h, launch e, inhale b, strain k, epidemic l, focus on j, complacency i, deteriorate a, legitimately c, drug-resistant g

1 dwarfs/dwarfed 2 fuelled 3 drug-resistant, epidemic, deteriorating, complacency 4 strains

Adjectives and nouns

1 six-month course 2 closed environment
3 effective treatment, drug-resistant strain
4 immune system 5 urgent problem

Verb phrases

1 mark 2 take 3 catch 4 inhaling
5 dwarfs 6 launch 7 focus(s)es/focus(s)ed
8 facing 9 increased 10 spreading

Prepositions

1 of the risk 2 from tuberculosis, in population 3 at risk, about tuberculosis

TB 'will kill 30m in next 10 years'

WHO warns of drug-resistant strain of disease

Tuberculosis is *spreading* rapidly throughout the world and is killing more people than at any time *in* history, the World Health Organisation said yesterday.

British specialists said that the *number* of cases in Britain had increased every year *since* 1986 and there had been *reports* of drug-resistant TB which was difficult and *expensive* to treat.

A new report by the organisation, *launched* in London yesterday to *mark* World TB Day on Sunday, said that the disease would kill 30 million people over the next 10 years. Yet *effective* treatment was available for £7 per person in some parts of the world.

TB was the most *urgent* health problem *facing* the planet, *dwarfing* fears about the ebola virus or BSE, yet there was still huge *complacency* in many countries.

Paul Nunn, chief of research for the organisation's *global* TB programme and a former specialist at Hammersmith Hospital, London, said: "The population of Britain is legitimately *concerned* about BSE, but reports *focus* on 10 cases of CJD which may be *related* to this." There were about 6,000 cases of TB a year in Britain and 400 deaths.

Arata Kochi, director of the TB programme, said the position had *deteriorated* over the *past* three years despite the organisation declaring TB a global health emergency in 1993, the first time it had *ever* so identified a single disease. Some 80 countries were using an effective treatment *programme* under which patients were supervised when *taking* drugs to ensure they *finished* the *six-month* course, but many could not afford this.

"We knew three years ago that tuberculosis had become the world's greatest killer of adults. We also know that a third of the world's *population* was already infected, with an additional *person* being infected every second. Three years ago we *warned* that the TB *epidemic* would become much worse. It has."

TB was the *biggest* single killer of women across the *globe* and a third of people with HIV died from TB.

"Anyone can *catch* tuberculosis simply by inhaling a TB *germ* that has been coughed or sneezed into the air. In a *closed* environment, they can remain alive for *up to* three years. There is nowhere to *hide* from tuberculosis. We are all *at* risk."

The disease had killed 2.1 million people in 1900, but today, because of the *increase* in population, the rise of HIV, which weakens the *immune* system and the failure of control programmes, TB was killing 3 million people a year. Poor treatment control programmes were fuelling drug-resistant *strains*. These were extremely difficult to *treat* and some cases were *incurable*.

"With *continued* neglect and inaction, deaths *from* TB may continue to rise and kill well *over* 100 million people in the next 50 years."

Chris Mihill in *The Guardian*

Expressions with *problem(s)*

1 no 2 faced 3 solved, presents 4 tackle
5 weight 6 child 7 poses

More collocations

1 caught, e 2 face, m 3 caught, o
4 face, g 5 deteriorated, c 6 launched, b
7 caught, l 8 launched, j 9 fuelled, h
10 deteriorating, k 11 launched, f
12 catch, n 13 facing, a 14 caught, d
15 fuelled, i

Unit 8

asbestos h, belated b, bronchitis j, hysteria f, dogged c, expose e, indestructible d, inhalation a, miracle i, prosecution g

1 miracle 2 prosecution 3 exposed
4 dogged 5 hysteria 6 belated
7 inhalation

Noun phrases

1 miracle substance 2 heavy cost 3 dogged insistence 4 wishful thinking 5 press hysteria 6 official response

Verb phrases

1 tighten safety standards 2 gave repeated assurances 3 taking prompt action
4 set up a government inquiry, do a comprehensive study 5 followed the familiar pattern

Verbs and nouns

carry out research, bring a prosecution, consult a doctor, enforce regulations, mark the beginning, do damage, take trouble, get a disease

Prepositions

1 of 2 on 3 of 4 on 5 against 6 for
7 to 8 to 9 of 10 on 11 on 12 of

It took 80 years to act

The 33-year-old man who came to *consult* Dr Montague Murray at London's Charing Cross Hospital seemed at first to be just another *victim* of bronchitis. But then he mentioned that the other nine men who had worked with him spinning the new *miracle* substance, asbestos, had all died in their thirties of the same condition. When he, too, perished less than a year later, Dr Murray found the heavy scarring of the lungs that came to be called asbestosis.

The year was 1899, and more than 80 years *passed* before asbestos use was *properly* regulated – a delay that allowed the killer dust to be spread so *widely* that most people in industrialised countries now have it in their lungs. The *official* response to the asbestos risk *followed* a familiar pattern: repeated *assurances* of safety; a dogged *insistence* on proof of damage to health; accusations of press *hysteria*; a failure to *carry out* research and then belated, *poorly-enforced*, half-measures. Afterwards came the *heavy* human and economic cost of failing to take *prompt* action.

Asbestos is *extraordinary* stuff; fire *resistant* and *virtually* indestructible yet so fine and pliable that it can be spun like cloth. But its fineness makes it easy to breathe in and its indestructibility lets it stay in the lungs, and *do* damage, over decades.

Its value and danger have *long* been known. It was used 4,500 years ago to strengthen clay pots, while the elder Pliny noticed that slaves who worked with it *got* lung disease. But it was not until 1879 that the mineral *embarked* on its *deadly* conquest of the world, when Samuel Turner, a Rochdale businessman, spun 10 tons of it to lag steam engines.

The complacency and wishful *thinking* began soon afterwards. Dr Murray *reported* on his asbestos victim to a government *inquiry* in 1906, but added: "One hears that *considerable* trouble is now taken to prevent the inhalation of the dust so that the disease is not so likely as heretofore."

No *comprehensive* study of British asbestos workers was done until 1928. When this found that 80 per cent of those who had been in the industry for over 20 years had asbestosis, the Chief Inspector of Factories *promised* the industry would be "safe" within a decade. It was not. The first regulations appeared in 1931, but they were insufficient and *unenforced*. In the next 38 years, while workers died by the hundreds, only two prosecutions were ever *brought*.

Lung cancers caused by asbestos were reported in the mid-1930s and found to be common 10 years later, but the link was not *considered* proved until 1955. Long-*awaited* regulations in 1969 aimed to provide *protection* against asbestosis – and failed. Their "safety" levels were *based* on a single study; one of the men who did the study admitted to me later that it was "not *adequate* for the purpose".

A series of articles in the *Yorkshire Post* in 1974 exposing an asbestos factory where more than 250 workers died *marked* the beginning of the end. The local MP started a campaign which led to a devastating inquiry and, eventually, to safety *standards* being so tightened that production effectively stopped. But by then the *damage* was done.

Geoffrey Lean in *The Independent on Sunday*

Adjectives and adverbs

Many time adverbs do not end in -ly, *such as in this article:* then, when, later, now, afterwards, long, ago, soon *and the rather archaic* heretofore.

Adjectives ending in -ly *used in the article are:* deadly *(line 17), and* likely *(line 21), which can also be used as an adverb.*

1 ugly 2 friendly/neighbourly
3 weekly/monthly, daily (*These three are also used as adverbs.*) 4 poorly *(Cannot be an adverb with this meaning.)* 5 friendly
6 cowardly/silly 7 fatherly 8 slovenly

Compound nouns and adjectives

1 hard-earned 2 half-hearted 3 hard-hitting
4 hard-wearing, half-price 5 long-standing
6 long-winded, long-drawn-out, half-truths
7 long-suffering, half-baked 8 half-light, long-lost 9 long-range

Unit 9

gaze e, freeze c, surveillance h,
ludicrous b, phenomenon k, predators l,
implication d, orthodox j, designed f,
superstition g, scan i train (on) a

1 implications 2 orthodox 3 superstition
4 surveillance 5 gazing 6 designed
7 froze 8 trained

Noun phrases

1 military surveillance 2 surveillance cameras
3 security manager, closed-circuit television
4 telescopic sights (*Not used:* living creatures)

Adjectives and nouns

1 scientific study, orthodox scientists
2 random chance 3 great advantage
4 profound implications 5 strong sense

Verb phrases

1 takes 2 performed, gathered, obtained,
3 pick up 4 proved 5 detect 6 developed

Sixth sense helps to watch your back

As the security *manager* of a large company in London, Les Lay has caught thousands of people on his surveillance *cameras*, and he is in no doubt: some people have a 'sixth sense' of when they are being watched.

They can have their backs to the cameras, or even be *scanned* using hidden devices, yet still they become agitated when the camera is *trained* on them. Some move on, some look around for the camera. "Not everybody does it," says Mr Lay. "They tend to be people who look fitter, more alert generally."

The idea that some people can sense when they are being stared at has so far been *rejected* as ludicrous by *orthodox* scientists. But now researchers in England and America are taking the claims *seriously*.

According to Dr Rupert Sheldrake, a biologist and former research fellow at Cambridge University, the *phenomenon* has long been recognised in fields such as wildlife *photography* and military *surveillance*. "Some police teams are said to have a rule about not keeping people in *telescopic* sights too long because suspects may sense they are being watched," said Dr Sheldrake. "I have also heard from a soldier who said that he had a very *strong* sense of being watched while walking down an alley on patrol one night, and he later heard that he had *narrowly* missed being *ambushed*."

Dr Sheldrake is now *gathering* data on the staring phenomenon as part of a *scientific* study. He said: "From an evolutionary point of view, any creature that *develops* an ability to tell when it is being stared at by potential *predators* would have a *great* advantage."

According to Russell Hartwell, an award-winning wildlife *photographer*, some animals do appear to have such a sixth sense. In one case last year, he was watching foxes from a hide when one of them passed about 30 yards away. "As he trotted by he *suddenly* froze and looked *straight* at me," he recalls. "I was very well hidden and I'm 99 per cent sure he hadn't picked up my *scent* as the wind was in my favour. I *really* do feel he could sense he was being stared at."

In an attempt to put the phenomenon on a *firmer* base, Dr Richard Wiseman, a psychologist at the University of Hertfordshire, has *performed* experiments that are *designed* to measure staring sensitivity. The tests involve measuring the skin resistance of people sitting under the gaze of a *closed-circuit* TV camera. The aim is to *detect* any changes in skin resistance when the person is being watched by someone else via the TV camera. In four trials, Dr Wiseman *obtained* results indistinguishable from *random* chance. However, similar experiments by Dr Marilyn Schlitz of the Institute for Noetic Sciences in San Francisco *proved* positive.

According to Dr Sheldrake, positive results from such experiments have *profound* implications for science. "It would show that the mind is not just *confined* within the brain, but can extend beyond it." Dr Sheldrake believes that the staring phenomenon may be *explained* by the idea of 'morphic fields', which *invisibly* bind together all living *creatures*.

"If creatures do prove to be *sensitive* to being stared at, it would also show that scientists have to take far more seriously all the supposed folklore that they have so far dismissed as *superstition*."

Robert Matthews in *The Sunday Telegraph*

Sense and *sensation* vocabulary

1 sensation 2 senseless 3 sensation 4 sensitive 5 sensational, senseless 6 make sense 7 sensible, common sense 8 sensitivity, sensitively 9 senses, sixth sense, sensory 10 sense of humour 11 sense of time 12 came to your senses 13 sense 14 sensuous/sensual

More collocations

1 complete/total surprise 2 utter/sheer nonsense 3 profound/deep regret 4 huge/enormous (tremendous) disappointment (*Note:* tremendous *is usually positive.*) 5 spectacular/tremendous (enormous) success 6 full/complete satisfaction 7 acute/keen sense of smell

Unit 10

acute b, psyche k, arctic g, demoralising j, humdrum l, mundane l, prescribe c, neurosis i, physiological h, susceptible a, temperate d, transition f, vintage e

1 susceptible, arctic 2 acute 3 vintage 4 transition 5 physiological, neurosis, prescribed

Word formation

darkness, sickness, treatment, madness, boredom

lifestyle f, lifeless h, weekend a (*contrasting*), workload b, overloaded g, semi-darkness c (*contrasting*), high-risk d, changeless e (*contrasting*)

Expressions

1 record 2 records 3 degree/extent

Adjectives and nouns

1 human psyche 2 Artificial light, susceptible people 3 heavy workload, long weekend 4 acute condition 5 ultimate solution 6 temperate regions, lifeless earth (*Not used:* occupational psychology)

Noun phrases

1 record levels, demoralising effect, suicide rate 2 special term, arctic countries, danger period, winter blues (*Not used:* physiological explanation)

After the gloom, a lighter outlook

SAD (Seasonal Affective Disorder) is now a recognised disease, striking almost everyone to a greater or lesser *degree* in winter, and the long grey winter we have just been through in the UK has been one of the worst for it on *record*.

This January was apparently the most light-starved since *records* began, preceded by the tenth coldest December this century, which has a demoralising *impact* on the human *psyche*. The weather produced record *levels* of winter depression.

"There might be a physiological *explanation* for it," says Cary Cooper, professor of occupational psychology at the University of Manchester Institute of Science and Technology. "But I think it is probably more psychological in most cases, though some people do get it very *badly*."

Arctic countries have long had terms for the

winter *blues:* "Cabin fever" and "Lapp sickness" both describe a sort of madness of distilled boredom that comes over people after months in semi-*darkness* with nothing to do outside.

They also have a special *term* for the grey season of transition between winter and spring, when the snow has *receded* in patches, leaving gashes of raw, frozen mud all over the *lifeless* earth and the icicles *drip* inexhaustibly without ever melting. That season of transition is when the suicide *rate* really perks up.

In more *temperate* regions like southern England, there are likely to be less *dramatic* explanations for madness than the weather. Work, for instance. "The high-risk SAD *period*, from October to March, is probably the time of year when people's *workload* is heaviest," according to Professor Cooper. "People are working longer and longer hours, getting up in the dark, going to work in the dark; and there are all sorts of *reasons* why it might make people *feel* depressed."

It has been a *vintage* year for SAD on the other side of the Atlantic. On the east coast, around New York, even if everyone there is always ready to *seize* on the latest neurosis, they have also had a particularly long and *unremitting* season of transition this year. The insight from America, however, is that this can often be cured by moving *northwards* rather than south.

There may be a physiological explanation for part of this, says Professor Cooper. Most of Canada is *bright* with snow at the moment, and the physiological theory of SAD *claims* that it is the lack of light which depresses *susceptible* people. Hence it can be *treated* by putting sufferers in *special* treatment cabinets and *blasting* them with *artificial* light made up of frequencies of a delicious summer.

However, simpler and more *mundane* cures may work, too. "There are other ways than going to Canada," says Professor Cooper. "Perhaps the simplest solution is to *ensure* that you go somewhere where there is a lot of sun." Those people with serious physiological SAD might need several breaks during the *danger* period.

Any expert who *prescribes* winter breaks in the sun must know what he is talking about. But Professor Cooper's *advice* can be even more helpful than that: "I think it's about *changing* your lifestyle," he says. For those SAD *sufferers* whose condition is less *acute*, "it might be enough to get away for a *long* weekend to a nice hotel." Change is all most of us need to *escape* from a dull, *humdrum*, overloaded world, full of *black* skies.

If none of these methods *works*, then Professor Cooper, originally from Los Angeles, has an *ultimate* solution: send people from the UK to *experience* the changeless all-year-round summer smog of his home town. Then they will be thankful for an English winter.

Andrew Brown in *The Independent*

Seasonal expressions

1 Indian summer 2 winter sports
3 spring-cleaning 4 spring chicken
5 wintry conditions 6 autumnal (autumn) colours, autumn leaves 7 wintry showers
8 mild winter

More collocations

1 cold conditions 2 neat solution
3 heart condition 4 terrible condition
5 heat treatment 6 weather conditions
7 easy solution 8 peak condition
9 appalling conditions, rough treatment
10 special treatment

Unit 11

bush h, cull i, delinquent f, deplete d, deploy a, dysfunctional c, matriarchal e, poach g, thrive b

1 delinquent, dysfunctional 2 thriving
3 poaching 4 depleting

Definitions

1 herd 2 calves 3 warden 4 gang
5 surplus 6 purchase

Word formation

oversee e, infrasound d, onlooker a, afield b, wildlife c

1 afield, wildlife 2 onlookers 3 infrasound
4 oversees

Verb phrases

1 pay, issue, co-ordinate 2 restore, keep
3 searching, extend

Noun phrases

1 adjacent land 2 attitude problem 3 soft option 4 tremendous distance, African bush
5 rich vocabulary 6 game reserve, stable population, high density, annual cull
7 strict disciplinarian, juvenile delinquent

An elephantine problem

Elephants are one of the world's slowest-breeding animals; yet left to themselves, their population can *double* every 15 years. South Africa's National Parks Board, the body responsible for *overseeing* the country's *game* reserves, knows this. Although elephant *herds* in countries farther north have been depleted by *poachers*, those in South Africa – where poaching is *kept* under much better control – have thrived. So to keep the elephant *population* stable in the country's largest national *park*, the Kruger, its herds have been culled *annually* for the past 28 years.

To many onlookers such *culling* seems both cruel and unnecessary. As a *consequence*, groups such as the International Fund for Animal Welfare (IFAW) have been *searching* for ways to stop the culling. In *practice*, this means either moving *surplus* elephants to other places, or buying new land *adjacent* to the parks to let them wander farther *afield*. Indeed, IFAW has offered $2.5m to the National Parks Board for such land *purchases*.

Eventually, though, if the population in the Kruger is to remain *stable* without culling – or, indeed, if the numbers in other parks *reach* densities that are too *high* – many more elephants may have to be moved out every year.

Even ignoring the large amount of money this would *cost*, it is not a *soft* option. Moving elephants can be quite traumatic. Until recently, shifting adult elephants, who can *weigh* up to four tonnes, was impossible. The equipment could not *stand up to* their objections. So only the *younger* elephants could be transported. Even today moving adults is difficult. But elephant society is *tight* knit. If an entire family group is not moved together, the calves that do move can end up as *juvenile* delinquents — as the *wardens* of several private game parks that have imported young elephants to start off their herds have discovered to their cost. A *bunch* of dysfunctional adolescents with no social graces and serious attitude *problems* can be troublesome for a park. They *form* gangs; they *terrorise* other wildlife; and, to cap it all, they *hide* from the tourists.

There is now a *way* around this problem: move some adults too. In particular, moving a few *fully* grown females, even if they are unrelated to any of the youths, soon *restores* law and *order*. For elephants are matriarchal. Their herds are organised around *females*, who *issue* instructions and *co-ordinate* movements. Mature males tend to leave the herd and live *alone*.

Matriarchs are *strict* disciplinarians. Only 30% of what elephants say is *audible* to people — the rest of their conversation is below the *range* of human hearing. But females have a *rich* vocabulary for bossing their groups around, and they *deploy* it often. (Males, by contrast, are creatures of *few* words.)

Since infrasound can travel a tremendous *distance*, elephants do not get much privacy. They can hear each other from more than four kilometres away, even through the buzz of the African *bush*. On a still, clear, warm evening, just after dark, the sound may *travel* more than twice as far. Experiments have shown that elephants pay *attention* to these *distant* calls, standing *still* and spreading out their ears to listen. Lone males, when they hear a female in heat, will walk for several kilometres to try to find her.

For the moment, though, the arguments of humans are drowning out any throaty rumbles from elephants. Many people agree that *extending* the boundaries of *existing* parks and creating new ones would be a good idea. Fewer want to risk *taking* the animal-welfare money and running.

The Economist

Comprehension

True: 1, 2, 4, 5

False: 3 (It would be impossible to keep them separate.)
6 (They eat practically *any* vegetation.)
7 (It was fixed *arbitrarily*.)
8 (Not indefinitely, but temporarily, '*as a stop-gap*'.)

Unit 12

benefit/gain, cocktail/mixture, cram/pack, disadvantage/drawback, distend/stretch, ethics/morality, fate/lot, marvel/miracle, productivity/yield, quest/search

Lexical sets

Cattle: bovine, bull, cow, cud, dairy, herd, manure, sire, stall, udder
Poultry: beak, cage, cock, free-range, hen, (manure), peck

1 free-range hens 2 cages, beaks, peck
3 herd, sired, bull 4 cud 5 bovine

Expressions with prepositions

1 vaccinated against disease 2 bred by artificial insemination, crammed into cages 3 fertilised by/with manure 4 worried about animal welfare, quest for efficiency 5 open to the public, surrounded by a circle (*Not used:* calculated by computer, saved from starvation)

Noun phrases

1 Animal welfare, moral obligation 2 signalling device 3 dairy cows, selective breeding 4 Intensive farming, developing countries (*Not used:* artificial insemination, chemical cocktail)

Verb phrases

1 missing 2 improve 3 growing, boosted 4 produce 5 catch 6 having 7 make

Growing pains

Take two cows. One is a marvel of high-tech farming. It lolls in the straw in a giant shed at a farm-research centre outside London. It has been *bred* by *artificial* insemination and vaccinated against a variety of *diseases*. Round its neck is an electronic signalling *device* which opens its personal feed-bin. This animal *produces* 12,000 kg of milk every year, roughly twice as much as Britain's average *dairy* cow.

The other, nonchalantly chewing the *cud* on an organic *farm* in Oxfordshire, is surrounded by a *circle* of admirers, for today the farm is open to the public. This cow was sired by a live *bull*. It eats no manufactured *feed*, and its blood is *free* from drugs. Crops *grown* on the farm are *fertilised* by its manure, not by some *chemical* cocktail. The trouble is that the milk *produced* by this cow is more expensive than *intensively* farmed milk. Many visitors may be *inspired* by the cow's back-to-nature feeling. Fewer will buy its milk.

That is the dilemma *confronting* consumers throughout the world. Increasing numbers of people in rich countries *have* doubts about modern farming methods. But few, so far, are willing to give up the cheap *food* these methods have brought. Even fewer consumers in *developing* countries are willing to *make* the sacrifice, for farming technology has *saved* millions of them from starvation.

Though the *fashion* has yet to catch on in most developing countries, consumers in the rich world are *increasingly* worried about animal *welfare*. These groups *claim* that intensive farming is cruel. Their evidence *appears* strong. In a *quest* for efficiency, many modern farmers stick hens in *cages* so small that they cannot *scratch* the ground. Turkeys are *crammed* by their thousand into windowless sheds, their beaks *cut off* to prevent aggression. Pigs are confined to *stalls* which prevent them from turning around.

These *practices* are undoubtedly disgusting. Whether animals have rights, or whether people have *moral* obligations to animals, are questions for philosophy and *ethics* rather than for science. But science does have a *contribution* to make to this debate, if only to remind those who are concerned for the welfare of the animals that a shift away from *intensive* farming will not always *improve* the animals' lot. Given complete freedom, chickens in a *free-range* farm will often bully and *peck* at each other. They may also *catch* more infections because they can peck around in each other's faeces.

Recall the intensively farmed cow *mentioned* at the beginning of this article. It is part of a *herd* bred by ADAS, a British farm consultancy, to investigate ways of *boosting* yields without *damaging* the animals' welfare. Its enormous productivity is *explained* partly by *selective* breeding, but also by careful, individual management.

Every week the cows are weighed and put through a foot bath, to *avoid* foot infections. The mix of their diet is *calculated* by computer so that it includes the right *combinations* of nutrients. It is also designed to *encourage* the cows to eat amply (hence it *includes* molasses, a bovine delicacy).

In addition, the cows are milked three times a day – more than the average in Britain. This improves their *yield*, but may also *reduce* the discomfort they feel from overdistended udders. All this treatment *requires* more manpower and equipment than the *average* dairy herd, yet the profits per cow are still *higher*.

In sum, the *complaint* that high-tech farming is bad for animal welfare is only partly true. It is in danger of *missing* the point that technology has also brought *gains* for animal welfare and – on some farms – may continue to do so.

The Economist

Adjectives

Behind all these complaints about *modern* farming lies an assumption which is rooted *deep* in the minds of many people. This is that *modern* farming is a subversion of nature, and that plants and animals would in general do much better without *human* interference.

The idea has an *instinctive* appeal, especially to the many city-dwellers who long for a more *natural* existence. Yet it relies on a distinction between the human and the *natural* worlds which may not coincide with reality.

Many species depend on one another to survive. One way of interpreting the emergence of agriculture, some 10,000 years ago, is that humans and *domestic* animals have developed a mutually *beneficial* relationship. Many *wild* species now face extinction, but, thanks to agriculture, the world population of sheep and cattle exceeds 1 billion – a *spectacular evolutionary* success. None of this is to deny the drawbacks of *modern* farming. But it suggests that the "nature" to which so many people would like farmers to return is neither as *easy* to define, nor as *benign*, as is often imagined.

Comprehension

Sentences 1, 2, 3 and 6 are in agreement with the extract. Sentences 4 and 5 are not.

Animal idioms

1 dog, D   2 cows, B   3 cat, A   4 horse, E
5 cat, pigeons C

Review 2

UNIT 7

1 urgent problem
2 effective treatment
3 immune system
4 faced with a problem
5 poses the problem
6 face the music
7 faced the facts
8 launch such a cruel attack
9 fuelled speculation
10 situation rapidly deteriorated

UNIT 8

1 dogged determination
2 miracle cure
3 wishful thinking
4 prompt action
5 set up a government inquiry
6 embark on a new project
7 half-hearted attempt
8 long-range forecast
9 environmentally-friendly
10 repeated assurances (*or* assertions)

UNIT 9

1 profound implications
2 utter nonsense
3 orthodox medicine
4 living creatures
5 extra-sensory perception
6 sense of humour
7 narrowly missed
8 dismiss this as superstition
9 came to her senses
10 picked up the scent

UNIT 10

1 acute shortage
2 prescribe medication
3 records began
4 heavy workload
5 temperate regions
6 ultimate solution
7 record levels
8 suicide rate
9 special treatment
10 peak condition

UNIT 11

1 dysfunctional family
2 depleting the earth's resources
3 far afield
4 restore law and order
5 soft option
6 high population density
7 strict disciplinarian
8 attitude problem
9 game reserves
10 stable population

UNIT 12

1 animal welfare
2 moral obligation
3 selective breeding
4 intensive farming
5 developing countries
6 improve his lot
7 spectacular success
8 domestic animals
9 chewing the cud
10 free-range eggs

Unit 13

adverse i,   drought h,   drown g,   flood g,
incidence c,   marginal a,   spectre d,
stabilise b,   tension f,   update e

1 adverse, incidence   2 tension, spectre, marginal   13 update, stabilised

Word formation

tension, availability, possibility, environmental, global, atmospheric, tendency, distribution, expansion, pollution, emission, concentration

Adjectives and nouns

1 heavy rainfall 2 leading scientists, global warming, likely impact, developing countries 3 massive loss, increased tendency

Noun phrases

1 heat stress 2 fossil fuel, resource wars 3 climate change, rainfall patterns, computer modelling, pollution controls, greenhouse gases 4 polar ice sheets, rising sea level 5 average global temperature 6 major river systems 7 global food supplies

Global warming disaster 'on way'

Scientist warns of risks from rising sea levels

One of Britain's *leading* scientists warned yesterday that it might already be too late to prevent some of the world's most *densely* populated regions being drowned within a century by the sea *level* rise brought on by the burning of *fossil* fuels.

Southern China, Bangladesh and Egypt face massive *loss* of land and the spectre of millions of environmental refugees, Sir John Houghton, chairman of the Royal Commission on Environmental Pollution, told the Royal Society last night. Even if greenhouse *gas* concentrations were *stabilised* according to UN agreements, Sir John said, the seas would *continue* to rise for centuries.

In one of the most pessimistic updates *yet* on the likely impact of global warming, Sir John, chairman of the UN's Inter-governmental Panel on Climate *Change* and a professor of atmospheric physics at Oxford University, further warned that water supplies throughout the world would be *severely* affected.

Echoing the *latest* UN analysis, he said that resource *wars* over water *rather* than oil were a possibility. *Demand* for water had been increasing in nearly every country. There were already tensions in regions where major river *systems* were shared between countries.

Global food supplies might not be severely affected by global warming, said Sir John. "Some regions may be able to grow more, others *less*, but the distribution of production will change because of changing water *availability*. The regions likely to be adversely *affected* are those in *developing* countries in the sub-tropics with rapidly *growing* populations. In these areas there could be large numbers of environmental refugees."

Forests and other ecosystems would not easily *adapt* to a wetter, warmer world, he said. Health would *suffer*, with more *incidence* of heat stress. Diseases like malaria would *become* more common.

Without pollution *controls* it was expected that *emissions* of carbon dioxide (the main global warming gas) would *increase* from a present 6 billion tons of carbon dioxide a year to about 20 billion tons a year in just over a century. This, he said, could mean a rise in average *global* temperature of 2.5°C – "a change of climate more *rapid* than has been *experienced* by the earth at any time in the last 10,000 years".

Most of the sea level *rise* would not come from the melting of the polar *ice* sheets but from the expansion of water in the *oceans* because of *increased* temperatures.

Sir John emphasised that while computer climate *modelling* was becoming more exact, it was still difficult to *predict* in detail on a small *scale*. All models of a globally warmed world, he said, suggested an increased tendency to *heavy* rainfall and the greater possibility of floods and droughts. The areas most *likely* to be affected by changing rainfall *patterns*, he said, were south-east Asia and those with marginal rainfall.

John Vidal in *The Guardian*

Vocabulary with *up-*

1 upright, uphold 2 uphill 3 uprising 4 uprooted 5 upfront 6 upkeep 7 upturn 8 upgraded 9 uplifting 10 upbringing

More collocations

1 densely populated 2 severely limited, completely exhausted 3 badly damaged, seriously injured 4 heavily defeated 5 highly publicised 6 strongly opposed

Unit 14

accelerate l, aquifer h, biosphere i, deplete m, drainage j, fuel d, mahogany e, outstrip a, prairies g, resources b, sludge c, soil k, timber f

1 sludge, drainage 2 depleted 3 fuel, outstrips 4 accelerate, biosphere, soil 5 resources

Noun phrases

1 copper mines 2 urban growth 3 global warming 4 wheat prairies 5 surrounding hills 6 land surface 7 populous cities

Verb phrases

burn oil, complete a study, cover an area, draw water, emit carbon dioxide, fell forests, pay the price, resolve a conflict, shape the future, take an interest

More noun phrases

1 the turn of the century 2 ways of coping 3 the quality of life 4 a layer of mud 5 a stack of timber 6 a series of films, the destruction of the rainforests

The greedy cities

Peering through a camera *lens* at a pile of timber turned Herbert Giradet from a film-maker into a professor.

It happened in the Brazilian port of Belem while he was making a *series* of films on the *destruction* of the rainforest. Tracking the camera along a *stack* of mahogany being swung into a freighter, he noticed the word "London" *stamped* on it. "I suddenly realised the impact that cities had on the world. I started to *take* an interest in the *connection* between urban consumption and human impact on the biosphere."

Now Professor of Environmental Planning at Middlesex University, he has just *completed* a study of London's *effect* on the planet. He has found that although it *covers* less than 400,000 acres, it needs nearly 50 million acres – 125 times its area – to *provide* it with food, timber and other resources and to absorb its pollution. "This means that, although it contains only 12 per cent of Britain's population, London requires an area equivalent to all the country's productive land to *service* it – though, of course, this extends to the wheat *prairies* of Kansas, the tea *gardens* of Assam, the copper *mines* of Zambia and other *far-flung* places."

The city, he calculates, *burns* the equivalent of two supertanker *loads* of oil every week and takes 1.2 million tonnes each of timber and metal, over 2 million tons each of food, paper and plastics and 1 billion tons of water every year. In return it churns out more than 15 million tons of *waste* and 7.5 million tons of sewage sludge annually – and *emits* 60 million tonnes of carbon dioxide as its contribution to *global* warming.

Similar calculations could be done elsewhere. Vienna takes in so much material that it *adds* 36,000 tons to its weight every day. Aligarh city in India imports 1,000 tonnes of soil daily for use in construction, affecting natural *drainage* and thus increasing flooding in the *surrounding* region. Mexico City has sunk by more than 20 feet over the last century because it has *drawn* so much water from the aquifer beneath it. And an expanding "ring of destruction" surrounds many African cities as trees are cut down to provide people with *fuel*. "In all," says Giradet, "cities occupy 2 per cent of the world's land *surface* but use some 75 per cent of the world's *resources* and release similar percentages of wastes."

Cities have always depleted the environment around them and have often *paid* the price. When archaeologists *excavated* Ur in Mesopotamia – one of the world's first cities – they found it had been buried by a *layer* of mud around 2,500 BC, the result, it is thought, of flooding caused by *felling* forests in the surrounding hills. The *fall* of Rome may have partially resulted from exhaustion of cropland. "Hell," wrote Shelley, "is a city much like London – a *populous* and smoky city."

But there has never been anything like the present *explosive* urban growth. The number of people living in towns and cities will *outstrip* those in the countryside for the first time in human history by the *turn* of the millennium. Within another 30 years there will be twice as many urban as country people.

"The future of humanity will be *shaped* largely by urban conditions," writes Professor Klaus Topfer, the German minister of urban development. "The *quality* of life for *generations* to come – and the chance to *resolve* conflict within nations and between them – will depend on whether governments find ways of *coping* with accelerating urban growth."

Geoffrey Lean in *The Independent on Sunday*

More vocabulary in context

Pushed by rural poverty and *official* neglect of the countryside, *pulled* by the hope of a *better* life in the cities, tens of millions of country people uproot themselves every year to join the *swelling* urban slums. The migrants find no houses *waiting* for them, no water supplies, no sewerage, no schools – and no welcome, for they are usually *resented* by wealthier citizens and *ignored*, at best, by the authorities. They have to settle on land no one else wants, that is too wet, too *dry*, too steep, or too polluted for *normal* habitation. They throw up *makeshift* hovels, made of whatever they can find – sticks, fronds, cardboard, tar-paper, petrol tins, perhaps (if they are lucky) *corrugated* iron.

Worldwide, the UN estimates, at least 250 million *urban* dwellers cannot get *safe drinking* water and many of those who do have to rely on standpipes that run for only a few hours a day. By 2000, most children *born* in Third World towns will be to such desperately *poor* families. Already more than 100 million *homeless* children struggle to survive on the streets.

Rich-world cities have ceased to grow rapidly, but their *relative* prosperity has brought its own swiftly *increasing* problems, quite apart from their enormous impact on the world's environment and resources. Pollution from car exhausts has raised death rates in cities all over the *industrialised* world. Meanwhile congestion has limited traffic to *average* speeds *slower* than in the days of the horse in cities as *diverse* as London and Milan, Utsunomiya in Japan and Trondheim in Norway.

Increasingly, cities are suffering simultaneously the problems of poverty and affluence: pollution and destitution. Worldwide, more than one in every three urban dwellers – 1.1 billion people – have to breathe *unhealthy* air. Many *inner* cities of the industrialised world are *sunk* in *dire* poverty. Men have a *better* chance of living to 65 in Bangladesh, the world's 12th *poorest* country, than in Harlem, New York, part of one of the *wealthiest*. It is *hard* to imagine the cities long being able to withstand *existing* pressures, let alone accommodating the *explosive* growth of the *next* decades.

Unit 15

disperse j, era c, fossil i, habitat k, indispensable b, orbit e, perspective l, pinpoint d, ramification f, reproduction a, slick g, smog h

1 pinpoint 2 era 3 perspective 4 indispensable 5 reproductions 6 ramifications 7 habitat 8 dispersed 9 smog 10 orbit 11 slick 12 fossil

Verb phrases

1 see, take 2 launched, orbit 3 extend, leave 4 play, pinpoint

Adjectives and nouns

1 live broadcast 2 indispensable tool 3 local problems, global warming 4 dispassionate observer 5 thick smog 6 swirling clouds 7 powerful symbol

Noun phrases

1 weather forecasters, oil slick 2 ecology movement, ozone layer, fossil fuels, power stations, acid rain (*Not used:* map makers, home planet, launch pad)

A new view of home

Once a photograph of the Earth, taken from the outside, is available ... a new idea as powerful as any in history will be let loose.

The astronomer Fred Hoyle *wrote* those words as long ago as 1948. It was a remarkable *prophecy*, the impact of which we are still feeling today. Cheap *reproductions* of photographs of our planet from space are so *widespread* now that we almost take them for *granted*. But that does not diminish their practical and *psychological* impact. They have become *indispensable* tools for *weather* forecasters and *map* makers, environmentalists and prospectors, global statisticians and spies. They have also stimulated a *sense* of awe and *wonder* in millions and especially in the few hundred *astronauts* and cosmonauts who have *seen* the view first-hand. It is a perspective on our planet that makes it seem very fragile and alone in the *vast* blackness of *space*.

It is hard to *pinpoint* exactly when that first image of the Earth as a whole, *taken* from space, was seen here. The first weather satellite, Tiros 1, was *launched* in April 1960 and returned 23,000 photographs. But that and all the other craft in low-Earth orbit were still too *close* to the planet to take it all in at once. They *extended* our horizons, but the cameras had hardly *left* home. In 1966, the US weather satellite Essa 1 became the first to be able to fit the *entire* globe into a *single* picture, from its *orbit* 900 miles up.

The true impact of seeing the home *planet* as a tiny, *isolated* ball did not come until Christmas 1968 when Frank Borman, Jim Lovell and Bill Anders *orbited* the Moon in Apollo 8. Their *live* broadcast on Christmas Eve, according to Jim Lovell, was *heard* by the largest audience that had ever *listened* to a *human* voice. Their photograph of "Earthrise" from above the Moon *became* the image of the era.

By the 1970s, the image of the Earth from space had become a *symbol* of the new global *ecology* movement. Until that time, many had thought of pollution as a local *problem* – a *thick* smog that would blow away, or an oil *slick* that would disperse in a limitless ocean. Suddenly, the Earth had limits and the image served to *emphasise* the interconnectedness of everything on it. It was at this time that awareness grew of how acidic *gases* from power *stations* in one country could fall as *acid* rain and damage the lakes and *forests* of another nation. It was then that the possibility of global *warming* as a result of the burning of *fossil* fuels and the destruction of forests began to be taken seriously. It was observations from space that first showed a hole in the ozone *layer* above Antarctica – though it took measurements from the ground to make people believe what the satellite showed.

The British space scientist and ecologist Professor James Lovelock believes that image of the Earth as a *tiny* ball with *swirling* clouds has become an icon almost as *powerful* as the cross or the crescent. Out of the images of the Earth, *concepts* such as "deep ecology" were born – the ecology not just of one small habitat but of all the interactions and ramifications that affect it, including the effects of humans. Suddenly, human beings were no longer the *dispassionate* observers of it all; they were part of the system part of the planet – and, in the new ecology, they have a compassionate role to *play*.

Martin Redfern in *The Independent on Sunday*

Vocabulary of prediction

1 foresee 2 forecast 3 prophesied
4 predicted 5 prophetic 6 unpredictable
7 unforeseen 8 foreseeable 9 foresight
10 forecast

More vocabulary in context

Since 1968 more than 3,000 men and women have been able to *admire* the view of Earth from space first-hand, and a surprisingly large number of them *admit* that the experience has *had* a profound and *lasting* effect on them.

The experiences of Sam Durrance are typical. He *took off* in Columbia in December 1990 after no fewer than five launch delays. Among the moments Durrance *picks out* are the salty sea breeze on the launch pad as he *waited* to *climb* aboard; the feeling of calm anticipation when *lying* on his back *awaiting* the final launch command; the creaking and *groaning* of the whole structure as the main engines *ignited* and the shaking acceleration as the solid rocket boosters *lifted* it from the pad. Only a few minutes later, the noise and acceleration *die* away and suddenly, almost surprisingly, you *discover* you are weightless. Then, at last, there is time to *look* at the view. This is the experience Durrance will never *forget*.

"That's the one thing nobody can *prepare* you for," he said. "Nothing can *prepare* you for what it actually *looks* like. The Earth is dramatically beautiful when you *see* it from orbit, more beautiful than any picture you've ever *seen*. It's an emotional experience because you're *removed* from the Earth but at the same time you *feel* this incredible connection to the Earth" – and here his voice *falters* – "like nothing I'd ever *felt* before."

Unit 16

1 migrants 2 macho 3 spouse, gender
4 ancestors 5 spick and span
6 Immaculate 7 myth, tale 8 forage
9 Strait 10 pelt 11 mammoth 12 whack

Noun phrases

1 fragments of bone, food remains, nuts and berries 2 big-game hunting, women and children, gender roles 3 out and about
4 chain of mountains 5 leopardskin pelt
(*Not used:* plants and animals)

Adjectives and nouns

1 distant ancestors 2 human settlement, north bank, tropical forest 3 traditional view, sole provider, macho hunter, hairy mammoth, latest evidence (*Not used:* marital home, distant past)

Verb phrases

1 fire, tasks 2 food 3 conclusions, evidence, theories 4 history, idea
5 remains, traces

Cave women

We have long been accustomed to the idea of the caveman as the *macho* hunter-gatherer, out and about all day whacking *hairy* mammoths while his hausfrau *spouse* keeps the cave spick and span. But Professor Anna Roosevelt, a Chicago archaeologist, has *journeyed* into the Brazilian Amazon and discovered *traces* of an 11,000-year-old politically *correct* primitive *human* settlement, where the food remains show a culture based on gathering *nuts* and berries. These tasks, says Professor Roosevelt, could just as easily have been *carried out* by women or even *children*. How intriguing that in the Americas of long ago, a *distant* ancestress of Hillary Clinton – her leopardskin pelt *immaculately* tailored – showed the way to the role-sharing *culture* American woman so enjoys today.

Stone Age hunters and the oldest wives' tale

It is one of the most enduring images of our distant *past* – Stone Age man, *dressed* in bearskin, *dragging* home the day's kill to the *grateful* wife as she minded the fire in the marital *cave*. Unfortunately, it is also probably untrue. Not only was the woman as likely to go out *gathering* food as the man, but their supper was *less* likely to be char-grilled mammoth than a few *small* reptiles or birds.

The *myth* of the hunger-gatherer male and the *domesticated* female is the creation of Victorian England, according to an American archaeologist. Professor Anna Roosevelt, of Chicago's Field Museum, is reported to have uncovered *evidence* in Brazil which *undermines* the idea that 11,000 years ago man was the *sole* provider.

Her expedition discovered food *remains* in a cave on the north *bank* of the Amazon in Monte Alegre which included small and young animals – which, she said, could *easily* have been caught and *killed* by women and children. "This culture didn't emphasise big-game *hunting*," she said. "The charred *food* remains we found point instead to broad-spectrum foraging."

According to Professor Roosevelt, earlier evidence that Stone Age people were big-game *hunters* was used by sociobiologists "to support a *genetic* basis for human behaviours such as aggression and certain *gender* roles." She added: "The claims of sociobiologists do *fit* Victorian England quite well. That is really where the origin of their theories *lies*."

However, Dr Robin Boast of Cambridge University said Professor Roosevelt may be *jumping* to conclusions – even if she is probably right. "To suggest from her finds that you should *rewrite* the history of gender *relations* – that's pushing it a bit," he said.

Professor Roosevelt's team *found* evidence of early human habitation in the *lowest* levels of the cave, including cave paintings and the carbonised remains of plants and animals. As well as fruit and wood from common *tropical* forest trees and *palms*, there were also *fragments* of bone from large forest game and fish, birds, reptiles, amphibians, smaller fish and game.

The discoveries could also mean that *theories* on how the Americas were populated will have to be *revised*. The *traditional* view is that the first migrants came across the Bering Strait from Asia, *settled* in the North American high plains and south-west, moving into South America down the Andean mountain *chain* later. The *latest* evidence suggests that a quite distinct culture from the original Palaeoindians *existed* at the same time, more than 5,000 miles to the south.

The London Evening Standard

Avoiding gender-specific language

1 them 2 police officer, firefighter 3 flight attendants/cabin crew 4 unanimously, chair(person) 5 salesperson/sales rep(resentative) 6 humanity/human beings 7 Ms 8 (an) artificial 9 person 10 humanity/human beings

Idioms

1 mother 2 brother 3 grandmother 4 man, man 5 man 6 lord 7 boy, girl 8 boy 9 men, boys, 10 boy 11 mother 12 grandfather 13 Brother

Unit 17

anomaly, j, crave i, envision f, hail b, honour a, poverty d, reappraisal e, renewal c, visionary h, write off g

1 hailed, honours, poverty 2 write off, renewal, reappraisal 3 envisioned

Word formation

self-contained b, post-war a, full-time e, multi-storey d, lieutenant-commander c

countryside, downtown, farmland, mainstream, marketplace, neighbourhood

Noun phrases

1 health care/crime prevention, training programmes 2 shopping mall 3 town square, property development (*Not used:* vegetable garden, family house)

Adjectives and nouns

low income c, late sixties f, moral imperative e urban renewal g, inner city a, racial diversity b, affordable housing d

Specifying noun phrases

1 ...14,000 acres of farmland 2 ... years of neglect 3 ...the concept of racial diversity 4 ...the quality of civic life 5 ...a billion dollars in loans

Verb phrases

tend the garden, coin a term, attend university, establish a foundation, improve the quality, make a profit, turn your attention, run an office

James Rouse

James Rouse was a visionary of *urban* renewal who developed the world's first shopping *mall* in Baltimore, built new towns in the US countryside and used the profits to *help* generate housing for the poor. An anomaly among developers, he *passionately* believed in the social benefit of his projects and his innovations forced the reappraisal of suburban growth and *inner* city organisation.

The son of a prosperous canned-foods broker, Rouse was taught to work *hard*, rising at dawn to *tend* the family *vegetable* garden. In 1930 his father died, leaving the family of five children with so many debts that the family *house* had to be sold. He *attended* the University of Virginia until 1933 when the Great Depression forced him to work *full-time* and continue his degree in law by studying at night.

His first job was *parking* cars in a *downtown* Baltimore garage. He *began* his career in 1936 at a branch of a Maryland mortgage office which he *ran* until 1939 before leaving to start his own firm, Moss-Rouse Company, financing single-family homes. After the Second World War, which he served out as a lieutenant-commander in the Naval Air Reserve in the Pacific, he expanded his *business* to shopping centres.

By the *late* 1950s, Rouse was using his *profits* to develop the nation's first enclosed shopping centre – Mondawmin Mall in Baltimore – *coining* the term "shopping mall", and thus he created the multi-*storey* mall and food court.

His most famous *development* was Columbia, a new town *built* on 14,000 acres of farmland outside Baltimore in the late sixties. *Based* on the concept of *racial* diversity and *intended* as a response to the chaotic post-*war* development of American cities, it was built as a self-contained community organised around nine small "villages", each *containing* several hundred houses and its own small shopping area. It now has 80,000 *residents*.

In the 1970s Rouse *turned* his attention to the inner *cities* which had been largely *written off* for commercial potential by developers. He envisioned the marriage of the suburban mall with the more *vibrant* life of a city street in self-contained areas he termed "festival marketplaces". The first, the Faneuil Hall area in Boston, *proved* to be exactly what tourists and *shoppers* craved – a comforting ideal of a town square in the centre of an unfamiliar city.

Throughout his career as head of the Rouse Company, one of America's most successful property development *companies*, he sought not just to *make* profits but to improve the *quality* of civic life.

After retirement in 1979 he began what he called "by far the most important work" of his life. The Enterprise Foundation he *established* sought to provide people with *low* incomes with good, *affordable* housing and the opportunity to lift themselves out of poverty into the *mainstream* of American life.

By 1994 the foundation had granted $1.7bn in loans and grants to develop more than 61,000 homes for low-income people and had expanded its charter to organise *training* programmes, crime-*prevention* efforts and health *care*. He held that helping neighbourhoods recover from years of neglect was not only a *moral* imperative but cheaper in the long *run*. "It's not enough to provide housing," Rouse said in 1991. "It's necessary to transform the neighbourhoods themselves."

In *presenting* Rouse with the nation's highest civilian honour, the Presidential Medal of Freedom, President Bill Clinton *hailed* him as an American hero who helped "heal the torn-out heart" of America's cities. "James Rouse's life had been defined by faith in the American spirit," he said.

Edward Helmore in *The Independent*

Register: formal vocabulary

1 prosperous, attended 2 vibrant, renowned, numerous/countless 3 most recent, work/opus, hailed 4 held, crave, seeking, transform 5 envisioned (*US English*)/ envisaged (*British*), haven/refuge/sanctuary 6 purchased, property, granted, construct 7 grew/became, rise, tend the garden

Register: words for people

Word groups: 2 family 3 guy/chap/bloke (fellow *is old-fashioned*), gentleman 4 girl, lady 5 boy, youth/young man 6 kids, infants 7 Dad (*used colloquially when addressing*)/old boy/old codger, senior citizen 8 friend, comrade/companion 9 boyfriend/girlfriend

Sentences: 1a persons 1b folk 2a kin 2b folks 3 bloke/chap/guy 4 girls 5 youth 6 kids, infants 7 senior citizens 8a mates/pals 8b comrades 9 boyfriend, fiancé

Unit 18

apocalyptic/catastrophic/lethal, breaker/wave, cataclysm/destruction/devastation/ruin, collapse/fall, create/generate, danger/hazard, detect/see, fairly/relatively, flank/side, huge/immeasurable, impending/threatening, imperceptible/invisible/unseen, monitor/survey, plot/scenario, slide/slip, unsound/unstable

Adjectives and nouns

1 apocalypse, cataclysm 2 catastrophes 3 volcanoes/volcanos

4 fractures, scar 5 idyllic 6 realm 7 devastation, eruption, catastrophic, lava 8 breakers 9 expedition 10 ridge

Word formation

1 landscape, landslide, mountainside 2 outrun 3 submarine

Noun phrases

1 geological fault, active volcano 2 shallow waters 3 mass destruction 4 disaster movies (*Not used:* holiday destination, potential hazard, tidal wave)

Verb phrases

1 bears/bore, blown 2 presented, crossing, caused 3 monitored, detect

Lethal shockwave from an island in the sun

It reads like the *plot* from a *disaster* movie. Florida is *devastated* by a tidal wave tens of metres high. The destruction and *loss* of life is immeasurable. The wave which *caused* so much devastation crossed the Atlantic in just a few hours, unseen until it *reached* the American coast. Its source is an unstable *geological* fault on the Canary Isles, more usually thought of as an idyllic *holiday* destination of thousands of European tourists than as the cause of disaster.

To ensure such a scenario remains in the *realms* of Hollywood, a group of British scientists *recently* travelled to the Canaries. By monitoring the fault which threatens to create the *tidal* wave, they hope to *predict* any hazard long before it could happen.

In the middle of the ocean these waves of mass *destruction* – called *tsunami* – are almost invisible. Only when they reach the *shallow* waters around coasts do they become *huge* breakers. The ruin caused by even a *relatively* small one can be apocalyptic. When the Krakatoa volcano *blew* itself to pieces in the last century, a *tsunami* six metres *high* killed 30,000 people.

Tsunami can also be generated when a huge landslide *falls* into the sea. This has never been seen in historical times but scientists have now identified the island of La Palma as a *potential* hazard.

"There is a *danger* that the side of the volcano facing west may fall into the Atlantic," says Professor Bill McGuire of the Centre for Volcanic Research in Cheltenham, who was part of the recent *expedition*.

"It could *literally* happen during the next few weeks or months or years," he said. "*Equally*, it could happen 100 years or more into the future. The island is very unstable and this is something which could happen *fairly* soon."

La Palma is not only the *steepest* island in the world but has also been the most *volcanically* active of the Canary Isles in the past 500 years. There have been two *eruptions* on the island this century *alone* – the last one was in 1971.

The volcanoes themselves do not *present* much danger. La Palma lava moves so *slowly* that most people could *easily* outrun it, so there is no *cause* for anxiety to the many tourists who *visit* the island. The real danger *lies* in the possibility that an eruption might trigger the *collapse* of a volcanic ridge which is unsound.

The problem started when an eruption in 1949 caused several cubic kilometres of rock to *slide* a few metres toward the sea. This also opened a two-kilometre-long *fracture* which can easily be seen to this day. There are not only *fears* that a *future* eruption would cause the rock to move again, but that next time, the landslide will not stop. If this happened, the resulting *tsunami* would be *catastrophic*.

"There have been three of these collapses in the *history* of the island," says Juan Carlos Carracedo of the Spanish National Research Council. Not only does the landscape bear the *scars* of these cataclysms, but submarine photos *show* rock from the *peaks* of old volcanoes far out to sea. "Another collapse is impending. The only way to prevent this hazard is to study the island *closely*."

By *monitoring* the change in shape of the mountainside, the team hope not only to discover if the western *flank* is slipping due to gravity, but to predict if the *sleeping* volcano is growing restless. Before eruptions, volcanoes always swell. This swelling may be *imperceptible* to the human eye. Only by surveying the shape of the ground with *sensitive* instruments can small *changes* be detected.

Phillip Henry in *The Independent*

Figurative meanings and more collocations

(L = *literal meaning*, F = *figurative or extended meaning*)

1 realms (F) 2 scenario (F) 3 fracture (L) 4 waves (F) 5 realm (L) 6 outran (L) 7 fractures (F) 8 realm (L) 9 scenario (L) 10 fractured (L) 11 outrun (F) 12 realms (F)

Isle or *island*?

1 Isles, islands, Isles, Isle, Isle 2 island 3 island 4 island 5 islands 6 Isle, island *(Note:* Isle *is more common in names and in poetry.)*

Review 3

UNIT 13

1 adverse weather conditions
2 heavy rainfall
3 fossil fuels
4 computer modelling
5 greenhouse gases
6 food supplies
7 sea level
8 uphill struggle
9 popular uprising
10 seriously/badly injured

UNIT 14

1 price to pay
2 take an interest
3 resolve the conflict
4 shape our whole future
5 quality of life
6 demand ... outstrip/outrun
7 cover ... area
8 dire poverty
9 corrugated iron
10 inner city

UNIT 15

1 launched ... satellite
2 extend his horizons
3 played a decisive role
4 live broadcasts
5 launch pad
6 take too much for granted
7 ecology movement
8 acid rain
9 oil slicks/spills
10 lasting effect

UNIT 16

1 old wives'
2 jump to conclusions
3 mother tongue
4 gender roles
5 revise their original theory
6 distant past
7 out and about
8 politically correct
9 big-game hunting
10 tropical forests

UNIT 17

1 Health care
2 training programmes
3 crime prevention
4 moral imperative
5 urban renewal/regeneration
6 racial diversity
7 improved the quality
8 next of kin
9 senior citizens
10 believed passionately

UNIT 18

1 idyllic scene
2 active volcano(e)s
3 geological fault
4 mass destruction
5 present new dangers
6 bears the scars
7 realms/bounds of possibility
8 worst-case scenario
9 desert island
10 monitors any changes

Unit 19

an abomination f, an air-miss c, in a blue funk b, palpitations d, smashed a, turbulence e

1 an abomination 2 palpitations 3 in a blue funk 4 smashed 5 an air-miss, turbulence

Hyphenated words

1 mid-40s 2 two-thirds 3 closed-in 4 mid-air 5 long-term 6 45-minute 7 self-hypnosis

Adjectives and nouns

vast numbers white knuckles, relaxed setting, clinical psychologist, closed-in space, wide-bodied jet

Noun phrases

1 tape recording 2 engine noise 3 panic attacks, relaxation techniques 4 consultant psychiatrist 5 success rate

Verb phrases

play a tape recording, join a course, take courage, board a bus, conquer the fear

Prepositions

1 in 2 on, by 3 about, with 4 with

Airport lessons put flying fear to flight

Courses offer happy landings to travellers grounded by terror

Fear of flying is no joke. A glance round any *plane* reveals white faces and white knuckles. Other sufferers may be *physically* sick, shake, sweat, have palpitations, faint, or even have mid-air *panic* attacks.

But now, attempts are being *made* to help such people cope with their fears. Captain Douglas Ord, a pilot, helps run British Airways courses for those who want to *conquer* the fear. He thinks newspapers and television have made more people frightened. "It is brought on by the disasterising and air-miss stories of the *media,*" he said.

Many of those who *join* the courses – which take a day and *culminate* in a 45-minute flight – have never been comfortable flying. "It's turbulence usually," Captain Ord said. "Nobody tells them what's going on and they get into a *blue* funk. We *aim* to get them to cope with flying."

The courses *run* approximately every six weeks. Those who attend are *aged* from 18 to the mid-40s, although some bring their children too. About two-thirds are women. "Men won't go on the course. They *get* smashed and sit there white-knuckled," said Captain Ord.

In the morning, the pilot *outlines* the technical aspects of the flight, explaining how the wings *work*, what the noises are and how the aircraft *deals* with turbulence. In the afternoon, a psychologist talks through the passenger's fears with them and teaches them *relaxation* techniques.

Dr Keith Stoll, one of the *clinical* psychologists involved, describes it as a "self-hypnosis de-sensitisation *process*". People may be afraid they are going to be sick or scream. To help them *control* their symptoms, they talk through the journey in the classroom – from leaving the room, to *boarding* the bus to the airport, to getting on the plane.

"We tend to get 90 per cent to 100 per cent of people on the plane," he said. "It takes a lot of *courage* to do it. Where the problem comes is that we don't know what the *long-term* success *rate* is. They may still feel uncomfortable. Most will go on to use flights again. Some come back for another course."

For those who *worry* about changing *engine* noises, they may suggest a *tape* recording which they can *play* to themselves in a relaxed *setting* at home. It may also help to take *trips* to the airport to watch planes taking off and *landing*.

Dr Michael Tarsh, a consultant *psychiatrist*, said: "It is *surprisingly* common. There are *vast* numbers whose holidays are made horrible for them because of the fear of coming back. Some people are afraid of being in a *closed-in* space. Clearly that is better in a *wide-bodied* jet. Then there are people who hate turbulence, like me. I don't take alcohol any more on planes because I faint and have to *lie* on the floor. Somebody always comes *along* and offers to help, saying they are a doctor. My wife says *icily*: 'So am I, and so is he'."

But for some people no amount of courses seem *likely* to succeed. "I don't believe the thing can stay in the air. I think it's an abomination of nature," was the *comment* of one whose feet seem *unlikely* ever to leave the ground."

Sarah Boseley in *The Guardian*

Hyphenated adjectives

1 cold-hearted, hard-hearted 2 kind-hearted 3 soft-hearted 4 even-handed 5 cool-headed 6 faint-hearted 7 heavy-hearted 8 heavy-handed 9 hot-tempered 10 small-minded 11 strong-willed 12 strong-minded

Idioms with colours

1 a grey area 2 a golden opportunity 3 through rose-tinted spectacles 4 saw red, purple with rage 5 once in a blue moon 6 in the black, in the red 7 born with a silver spoon in her mouth 8 red in tooth and claw 9 green with envy 10 the golden rule

Unit 20

anomaly/peculiarity, beacon/signal, circuitry/wiring, device/gadget, diverge/veer, exclude/rule out, far-fetched/incredible, hurtle/rush very fast, increasing/mounting, pile/stack

Word formation

1 remote-controlled, battery-powered 2 in-flight 3 cockpit 4 playback 5 cone-shaped 6 autopilot

Noun phrases

tape recorder, radio signal/equipment transmitter, flight path/recorder, laptop computer, cassette player/recorder, navigation beacon/computer/equipment/signal, compact disc player

Adjectives and nouns

1 in-flight movie, first class 2 wide variety, electronic gadgets 3 poor visibility 4 striking example 5 mounting evidence 6 tidal wave (*Not used:* certain amount)

Phrases with adverbs

land safely, return to normal, behave strangely, particularly concerned, first published, heavily computerized, firmly in control

Verb phrases

1 veered, crashed 2 emit, picked up 3 land 4 shook 5 lost, sounds, hurtling 6 puts 7 sets, turn off 8 tune

Hazards aloft

Unless you are born with feathers, flying requires a leap of faith. Passengers have to *assume*, when they strap themselves in, that a 227,000-kg machine hurtling through the air is *firmly* in the pilot's control. That faith was *shaken* last week by a report that a DC-10 coming into New York's Kennedy airport recently almost *crashed* when a passenger in *first* class turned on his portable compact disc *player*.

The story, first *published* in TIME, set off what one airline called "a tidal *wave*" of concern. Can jets really be *diverted* from their *flight* paths by something as small as a battery-*powered* CD player? Or a video-game machine? Or any of a dozen *electronic* gadgets and computers that passengers *regularly* carry on board?

Far-fetched as it may *sound*, it can't be *ruled* out. Every electrical *device* creates a *certain* amount of radiation. Portable phones, remote-control toys and other radio transmitters *emit* signals that can carry for kilometers, and their use on planes has *long* been banned. But most airlines still *let* passengers use *cassette* players, *tape* recorders and *laptop* computers, which make *far* less electromagnetic noise.

Now there is *mounting* evidence that even these gadgets may be *putting* aircraft at risk. A walkman-type radio *tuned* to an FM station generates oscillations that can extend 1.5m to 3.7m – far *enough*, in some planes, to reach the navigation *equipment* stowed in and around the cockpit. "With their thick wires and vacuum tubes, the old planes probably wouldn't feel a thing," says Bruce Nordwall, avionics editor of *Aviation Weekly & Space Technology*. "But the lowpower circuits in *modern* aircraft are much more *susceptible* to interference."

Pilots are *particularly* concerned about interference with the circuitry that *picks up* radio signals from the so-called VOR (visual omni-range) network – hundreds of cone-*shaped* navigation beacons *scattered* across the US. Automatic flight-control systems depend on clear VOR signals to land planes *safely* when visibility is *poor*. But some of that VOR equipment has been behaving *strangely* of late, occasionally causing aircraft on autopilot to *veer* sickeningly out of control.

No planes have crashed and no lives have been *lost* – so far. But TIME has obtained a *stack* of pilot reports linking a *series* of "anomalies" to a *wide* variety of *electronic* gadgets, from laptop *computers* to Nintendo Game Boys. In one *striking* example, a plane flying out of Chicago started veering off *course* while its VOR dials dimmed and danced around. When the passenger in seat 9-D *turned off* his laptop, the report *states*, the "panel lights immediately *brightened* dramatically and all navigation aids returned to *normal*."

The US Federal Aviation Administration, *pressed* by pilots to crack down on the gadgets, issued an advisory late last week that left it up to the airlines to *set* their own rules. Delta has already *expanded* its list of *forbidden* devices to include video playback machines and CD players. With the arrival of new "fly-by-wire" aircraft, which are *heavily* computerized and even more vulnerable to *interference*, passengers may have to go back to reading *paperbacks* and watching the *in-flight* movie.

Philip Elmer-Dewitt in TIME *magazine*

Spelling note: The American spellings *kilometer* and *computerized* are used in this article. The British equivalents are *kilometre* and *computerised.*

Hyphenated adjectives

1 multi-faceted, bare-faced 2 oft-repeated, new-mown, snow-capped 3 horn-rimmed, silver-framed 4 ivy-covered, old-fashioned, oak-panelled 5 new-laid 6 deep-fried

Register

1 extinguish, smoking material, refrain from smoking, illuminated 2 requested, proceed 3 belongings, disembark 4 address 5 alight

Unit 21

ardour/enthusiasm, cut/slash, desultory/unenthusiastic, fashionable/trendy, frenzy/madness, rise/soar, rush/scramble

1 monopoly 2 operators 3 entrenched 4 competition 5 slashed 6 promotions 7 bargains 8 market 9 boom 10 niche

Associations

Similar in meaning: craze/trend, rates/prices, numbers/rates, portable/mobile (cellular), leap/soar

Contrasting in meaning: lag/catch up, monopoly/competition, private/state-owned, challenger/entrenched operator, digital/analog, fixed-line/cellular (mobile)

Complementary or closely associated: ardour/frenzy, schools/classrooms, parents/kids

Verb phrases

1 keep 2 transmit 3 stepping up, grab, dominate 4 slash(ed), lap(ped) up 5 chat, keep 6 fuel

Adjectives and nouns

1 high-flying, trendy 2 digital, pricey 3 worldwide, digital

Noun phrases

1 summer house, ski slopes 2 market share, niche product 3 wireless spectrum 4 price war (*Not used:* car battery, computer data)

Have phone, can travel

The number of cellular-phone subscribers in Western Europe leaped 56% last year, to 23.4 million users and is sure to keep climbing. Once a pricey *toy* for *high-flying* executives, the mobile phone has broken into the personal market. Teenagers chat with their *friends*, parents use them to *keep* track of their *kids*, and the elderly carry them for an extra measure of *security*. The result has been dizzying *price* wars in Britain and phonophilia in Scandinavia, where portable handsets have become nearly as common as digital *watches*. Danish schools have even found it necessary to ban phones from *classrooms*. "This is no longer a niche *product*," says Lauri Kivinen, spokesman for Finland's Nokia, which, along with Motorola of the US and Sweden's Ericsson, dominates the hardware *market*.

The Euro-craze is part of a worldwide *trend*. Total global subscribers *soared* 57% last year, to 85 million, according to the International Telecommunications Union, and could *reach* anywhere from 200 million to 350 million by the year 2000. North America still *accounts* for about half the *world* market, but Europe, though *lagging* in subscribers per capita – save in Scandinavia – is fast catching up. Indeed it already *leads* the US in the use of digital *technology*, which is better at *transmitting* computer *data*, harder to eavesdrop on, and can fit more voice channels into the wireless *spectrum* than traditional analog systems.

Stepped-up competition is fueling the *boom*, as virtually every European country has added at least one new mobile *operator* to an industry that typically started out as a monopoly in each nation. Nowhere is this *competitive* frenzy more *evident* than in Britain, where four operators with six networks are deluging newspaper readers and TV viewers with *ads* for $15 handsets, free calling time, and other *promotions* to grab market *share*. Consumers are *lapping up* the bargains: the number of British mobile subscribers has doubled in 18 months to 5.8 million. France, normally gadget-happy, is a major laggard in the cell-phone *race*, thanks to desultory competition between state-owned France Telecom and *private* rival SFR.

In Italy, just the threat of challenger Omnitel coming on the scene sent entrenched operator Telecom Italia Mobile scrambling to *slash* rates. The resulting price *war* has put a *telefonino*, or little telephone, into the hands of 1 in every 6 Italians between the ages of 21 and 60. Italians chat on them in *trendy* restaurants, on the ski *slopes*, driving motorbikes or just walking down the street. It's a sign you've made it. After the car and the *washing* machine, you buy a *telefonino*.

Scandinavia, which pioneered international cell-phone connections in the 1980s, shows no sign of *losing* its ardor for mobile phones. In fact, just the opposite: *sales* exploded in Norway last summer, *pushing* subscriber rates to a European-leading 25.3% of the population, and the number of Danish mobiles doubled last year, to about 1 million, serving 18% of the people. Every third person in Stockholm now has a cell phone; Swedes often use portable models as the phones in their *summer* houses.

Teenagers are as addicted to going mobile as they are to *fixed-line* phones: "If I see a pretty girl at a disco, I like to *impress* her by talking on my mobile," says Copenhagen high-schooler Attila Zelikdemir. Even Denmark's vagabonds, who *roam* the countryside during the summer, use cell phones to *keep* in touch. "My wife didn't like the idea of my being so isolated on the road," says wanderer Sune Olsen. "She calls me up every second day." Recharging? No problem – Olsen carries a car *battery* in the pram he *pushes* along the highways.

Jay Branegan in TIME *magazine*

Spelling note: The American spellings *ardor* and *fueling* are used in this article. The British equivalents are *ardour* and *fuelling*.

-philia / -phobia

1 books 2 England and anything English 3 France and anything French 4 Europe (especially the European Union) 5 love of languages 6 fear of technology or fear of modern gadgets (such as mobile phones) 7 fear of foreigners 8 fear of light 9 fear of water 10 love of water 11 fear of enclosed spaces 12 fear of large open spaces

Advice matching

1E 2F 3B 4G 5C 6A 7D

Unit 22

assist/help, civil/public, crime/offence, debatable/equivocal, dramatic/sensational, drop/fall, example/instance, identify/pinpoint, immense/vast, level/rate, limit/restrict

Definitions

anecdotal h, borough f, campaigner j, compelling c, deterrent b, highlight g, Home Office e, ply a, rhetoric d, building society i

1 compelling 2 highlights 3 deterrent 4 campaigner 5 plying 6 anecdotal

Noun phrases

1 vehicle thefts, police investigation 2 radio pagers 3 city centre, security staff, crime rates, deterrent effect 4 building societies

More noun phrases

1 equivocal answer 2 compelling evidence, sensational headlines, public disorder 3 vast majority (*Not used:* limited use)

crime prevention measures, strong deterrent effect, civil liberties campaigner, closed circuit television, overall crime levels, multi-storey car park

Verb phrases

1 ply, drop 2 install, reduce, deter, commit 3 prevent, restricting 4 expressing, sound (*Not used:* convict the guilty, identify suspects, publish research)

Someone to watch over me

All over Britain, the closed circuit television camera – the spy in the street – is starting to help police with their inquiries. When the Home Secretary opened a CCTV scheme in the Lancashire town of Clitheroe last September he said: "The value of this technology is immense: it *prevents* crime from happening in the first place, assists *police* investigations, *identifies* suspects and helps *convict* the guilty."

In the decade since the first city-centre CCTVs were *installed*, politicians and the police have praised the cameras for their *role* in beating crime. Dramatic *drops* in crime rates have made some *sensational* headlines. But the *stories* have been anecdotal. Until last month no systematic *research* on the effectiveness of CCTVs had been published. Now three separate *studies* covering the effect of cameras in five different areas have been *made* public – one by the Home Office of CCTV schemes in Birmingham, King's Lynn and Newcastle, and two others of Airdrie in Strathclyde and Sutton in Surrey. For the first time it is possible to look in *detail* at the *facts* behind the rhetoric.

Undoubtedly the main *claim* for CCTVs is that the cameras *deter* criminals. But do they prevent crime? The answer is far from *clear-cut*. Two of the studies found a *drop* in crime. But although there was a 13 per cent fall in crimes in the part of Sutton covered by cameras, there was a *larger* fall in other parts of the borough because of other crime prevention *measures* such as *locking* multi-storey car *parks* overnight and giving security *staff* radio *pagers*.

The Home Office's own research produces a similarly equivocal *answer*. The research found "compelling *evidence*" that the cameras "had a strong *deterrent* effect" on crime in Newcastle. However, the report highlights "the failure of the camera system to *reduce* overall crime *levels* within Birmingham *city* centre". CCTVs do not work for all types of crime. *Burglaries* and vehicle *thefts* are offences which the cameras do seem to prevent. But they have less effect on vandalism, assaults and *public* disorder offences.

Richard Thomas, chairman of the Association of Chief Police Officers' committee on security cameras, *sounds* a note of *caution*. "There have been cameras in building societies for years and years and we still get people trying to *rob* them with nothing covering their faces," he says.

One of the problems common to all *crime* prevention schemes is that criminals may simply *ply* their trade elsewhere – a phenomenon known as displacement. An obvious *instance* of displacement came to light in the Sutton study, where *thieves* stopped stealing on the streets where they could be caught on camera and started *stealing* from people in shops instead.

Even if the effect of CCTV on crime prevention is *debatable*, do the cameras help police to arrest criminals and to convict the *guilty?* In King's Lynn the cameras were only of *limited* use in pinpointing the criminals. "In the *vast* majority of cases when officers requested tape reviews of areas where crimes had been *committed*, nothing of particular use had been *recorded* by the cameras," says the Home Office.

The *scale* of the introduction of CCTVs has worried *civil* liberties campaigners. The organisation Liberty says the cameras can *restrict* people's freedom to *express* opinions in public. Certainly, you might be forgiven for thinking that Big Brother is *watching* you in King's Lynn. The most common use of the cameras there has been to follow people who are *acting* suspiciously or who are "known *trouble*-makers". The Home Office researchers found about 800 such *instances*. No one was arrested. In King's Lynn, the cameras' most frequent success is catching people *dropping* litter or urinating in public.

Mark Ward in *New Scientist*

Legal vocabulary

1 penalties 2 trial, imprisonment 3 offence, jail, community, compensation 4 offender, caution, court 5 custody 6 prosecute, evidence

Connotation

1a got off scot-free 1b was acquitted
2a lenient 2b soft 3a lying 3b fib
4a insinuation 4b implication 5a fraud
5b impostor 6a expose 6b reveal
7a discreet 7b secretive 8a famous
8b notorious

Unit 23

commission f, dole h, ethic b, lavishly c, literacy d, nominally i, numeracy e, poach a, union j, workforce g

1 nominally 2 union 3 dole 4 literacy numeracy 5 ethic

Hyphenated adjectives

well-trained workforce, full-time education, post-modern society, out-of-work youths, large-scale programmes, job-search advice

Adjectives and nouns

1 faster growth, productive workforces
2 generous support 3 strong case, basic education (*Not used:* high unemployment)

Noun phrases

1 literacy rates, living standards
2 government intervention, training programmes
3 skills training

Verb phrases

1 address, raise, finding, improved
2 released, makes, understand 3 taught
4 received/receiving 5 spent
(*Not used:* pay the bill, increase demand)

Training and jobs: What works?

Many politicians assume that training is one of the best ways to get the jobless off the dole. The evidence suggests that it is not that simple.

On the face of it, the case for generous public *support* for training is *strong*. Unskilled people are much *more* likely to be out of work than *skilled* ones; if only their *qualifications* could be improved, they might *find* jobs more *readily*. Not only would they benefit, but so would the *economy* as a whole. A better-trained workforce would be a more *productive* one; so more training ought to mean not just *lower* unemployment but also *faster* growth and higher living *standards*. Unions like training *programmes* because they can use them to push up *wages*. Academics like them because they increase *demand* for more education. Parents like them because they give *out-of-work*, out-of-school youths something to do. Prophets of a *post-modern* society praise them as part of an ethic of *life-long* learning. And employers don't mind them because the public *pays* the bill.

As if all that were not enough, there is even a neat "market failure" argument to *explain* why privately *provided* training is bound to be inadequate. Why should firms pay to *equip* employees with *improved* skills when those workers can be *poached* at a moment's *notice* by competitors? The state must pay, or nobody will. Here, apparently, is a case where government *intervention* can do some good.

All in all, then, the *case* for publicly supported schemes seems solid. There is just one problem. In practice, they rarely *work*.

A notable experiment in America *compared* one group of unemployed people who *received* job-search advice with another that got advice plus a *place* on a training scheme. There was no difference in employment or earnings between the two. Another *piece* of evidence comes from Sweden, which also *spends* lavishly on training the unemployed, and is beginning to *wonder* whether the policy is worth it. Sweden's parliament commissioned three economists to *study* the country's long-admired "active labour-market programmes", including job search *assistance*, training and relief-work. The authors *concluded* that while retraining might raise, slightly, the chances of employment, it does so at higher cost, and to *less* effect, than simple job-search advice.

Large-scale training programmes *devoted* to the uneducated, unskilled and jobless might hope to *make* a big difference – but, as the evidence *shows*, do not. Often this may be because the skills that matter are more elementary than those *taught* in training schemes. If so, the priority should be to improve basic education and so *reduce* the numbers of hard-to-employ earlier in life. In a report *released* recently, Industry in Education, a British employers' group said that what they really needed was not more skills training but people able to *address* an envelope. An OECD *survey* released last year suggested that complaints about basic literacy are *widespread* even in countries with nominally high literacy *rates*. In Sweden, which *came off* best, one in 12 men could not *understand* the instructions on an aspirin *bottle*; in the Netherlands, the *figure* was one in ten; in Germany one in seven; and in Canada and America one in five.

There is good cause for providing *education* in basic literacy and numeracy for adults who need it.

But do not expect too much. Many of those who have spent ten or more years in *full-time* education without learning to read or add up may be beyond *help* of this sort.

The Economist

More vocabulary in context

training, true/so, workers/earners, positions/posts/jobs, job, moved, work/jobs, companies/employers/bosses, programme, adapt/respond/react, schemes/programmes, meet/satisfy, train, risk/danger, willing/prepared/persuaded, skills, in-house, well, public/government/state, supported/sponsored/financed/funded/backed/provided, search/look/retrain, skills (/education), education, likely, fall(s)/reduction(s)/drop, employers, levels/what

Actual text:

Once in work, on-the-job *training* (as opposed to out-of-a-job training) brings clear improvements in productivity and wages. That is *true* even for low-wage jobs. A study that followed American minimum-wage *workers* found that after three years of work, only 15% were still working in minimum-wage *positions* – and for many of those, the *job* was a second, part-time one. The rest had *moved* on. For those in *work*, in-house training seems to help mobility.

In-house training benefits *companies* as well as workers. That is why firms do it. Intel, for example, an American chip-maker, has a more or less continuous retraining *programme*, enabling the firm to *adapt* to the volatility of the chip business. Mass-training *schemes* administered by civil servants cannot *meet* such needs.

The conclusion seems to be that the supposed market failure of training is greatly exaggerated: firms will *train* workers, despite the *risk* of poaching, provided that workers are *willing* to meet some of the cost through lower wages, and/or that the *skills* concerned are firm-specific (i.e. not easily sold to another employer). For most workers in most firms, these conditions are met: that is why *in-house* training is alive and *well*, without benefit of *public* subsidy.

Where government-supported training programmes have succeeded they have been either small and focused, concentrating on helping people *search* for work, or else they have equipped people with basic *skills*. Arguably, the closer training is to general *education*, the more *likely* it is to succeed. But even if education and training are working as they should, expect no miraculous *falls* in unemployment until the costs of labour to *employers*, and the benefits of labour to workers, have been shifted to *levels* the market will bear.

Hyphenated adjectives

1 long-awaited tenth symphony 2 pre-cooked, oven-ready meals 3 three-month-long trial 4 easy-to-assemble cupboard, ready-made piece ... 5 soon-to-be-married/soon-to-be-wed (*especially common in newspapers*) 6 His new-found desire ... was very short-lived

Unit 24

1 state-of-the-art, hot (*informal*) 2 pangs 3 cool (*informal*) 4 throes 5 specificity 6 sequel 7 calling 8 guise 9 fringe 10 corporate 11 paradigm 12 workaday

Word formation

outcome a, counterculture f, forward-looking d, groundbreaking b, blockbuster c, mainstream e

Noun phrases

long-range forecasting, husband-and-wife team, traditional nuclear family, consumer-electronics products, sound scientific principles, bestseller list

1 cold war, environmental catastrophe 2 atom bomb, death throes 3 Social scientists, computer revolution 4 radical fringe, strategic analysis 5 birth pangs, 21st century (*Not used:* hard numbers)

Verb phrases

1 stood/stand in the shadow 2 brought (science) to the masses 3 appeared in the press 4 had a vision 5 set the standard 6 gave (his own stories) credibility 7 prevent (a possible) catastrophe (*Not used:* affect the outcome)

Cashing in on tomorrow

Who will fight the next war in the Middle East? Where will the best new jobs be found next year, and where will the most old ones be lost? What will be the hot consumer-electronics *products* of 2008? How will the Internet change commerce in the 21st *century?* Where will the next environmental *catastrophe* occur – and what can be done to *prevent* it?

These are the *kinds* of questions that are asked – and, for a price, answered – by the *forward-looking* folks who call themselves futurists. Once the calling of *wild*-eyed Cassandras and 19th century writers and *social* scientists on the *radical* fringe, long-range *forecasting* has become a sophisticated and quite profitable *industry*. Its practitioners *appear* increasingly in the press and on the best-seller *lists*. But they all *stand* in the shadow of Alvin and Heidi Toffler, the husband-and-wife *team* whose 1970 blockbuster, *Future Shock*, blasted the infant profession into the mainstream and *set* the standard by which all subsequent would-be futurists have been *measured*.

The Tofflers didn't *invent* futurism, of course. H.G. Wells, Jules Verne and George Orwell were all practicing futurists working under the science-fiction *guise*. Fittingly, perhaps, modern futurism was born with the *atom* bomb, in that moment when it was suddenly possible to *imagine* a world without a future. It was Hermann Kahn who *gave* the nascent profession credibility with such groundbreaking books as *Thinking About the Unthinkable* (1962), which used sound *scientific* principles to predict with great *specificity* the likely effects of a thermonuclear *war*.

But it was the Tofflers who *brought* futurism to the masses. *Future Shock* made the new profession *cool*. The book and its best-selling *sequels*, *The Third Wave* (1984) and *Powershift* (1990), *examined* not just tomorrow but today, not just one industry but all mankind, making the paradigm-shattering argument that what was really *changing* society was the radical acceleration of change itself. Future *shock*, the Tofflers said, is what happens when change *occurs* faster than people's ability to *adapt* to it. The book resonated for the 1960s counterculture, and in some ways it *echoes* even louder in the digital *era*. "People today," says Alvin Toffler, "are scared *silly*."

That's the great *thing* about pondering the future these days: there seems to be so much more of it. Between the computer *revolution* and the end of the *cold* war, between the birth *pangs* of the international economy and the death *throes* of the traditional *nuclear* family, the demand for solid, scientifically *based* forecasting is greater than ever. *Hard* numbers are difficult to come by since so much "futurist" work goes on under the guise of economic forecasting or strategic *analysis*, but corporate America clearly has the religion. People who used to have purely planning *titles* have been incorporated into other roles. If you're in management at a modern company and you don't *spend* at least part of your day thinking like a futurist, you probably aren't *doing* your job.

Paul Saffo, who in his decade with the Institute for the Future has consulted for everyone from the U.S. Defense Department to a Swedish on-line service, prefers to *distinguish* between "visionaries" – "people who have a *vision* of what the future should be and are trying to make it happen" – and workaday "forecasters" like himself. "My job is to help our clients expand their perceived *range* of possibilities," Saffo says. Of course, in that capacity, he acknowledges, "you can *affect* outcomes."

Sometimes, however, it's hard to separate *cause* from effect. "Futurism isn't prediction *anymore*," says Douglas Rushkoff. "It's state-of-the-art propaganda. It's future *creation*."

Michael Krantz in TIME *magazine*

Spelling note:
The American spellings *practicing* and *Defense* are used in this article. The British equivalents are *practising* and *Defence*.

Figurative expressions

1 hot 2 soft 3 hard 4 hot 5 cold
6 lukewarm/cool 7 hard 8 warm 9 hot
10 cool 11 hot 12 soft, hard-luck
13 warmed 14 hot

Compound adjectives

1 boggles the mind, mind-boggling
2 warmed my heart, heartwarming
3 took my breath away, breathtaking
4 breaks my heart, heartbreaking
5 blew our minds, mind-blowing
6 earth-shattering

Review 4

UNIT 19

1 mid-air collision
2 vast numbers
3 panic attack
4 relaxation techniques
5 conquer her fear
6 golden opportunity
7 grey area
8 cool-headed
9 golden rule
10 even-handed

UNIT 20

1 flight path
2 laptop computer
3 mounting evidence
4 wide variety
5 poor visibility
6 electronic gadget
7 veered off course
8 shakes your faith
9 sounds far-fetched
10 puts people's lives at risk

UNIT 21

1 keep track
2 keep in touch
3 boom was fuelled
4 transmit computer data
5 trendy restaurants
6 price war
7 high-flying executive
8 dominated the market
9 tabloid newspapers
10 job interview

UNIT 22

1 compelling (/convincing) argument
2 deterrent effect
3 effective deterrent
4 anecdotal evidence
5 crime rates
6 vast majority
7 equivocal (/evasive) answer
8 civil liberties
9 restrict (/limit) ... freedom
10 sounded a note

UNIT 23

1 generous support
2 strong case
3 basic education
4 full-time education
5 well-trained workforce
6 government intervention
7 living standards
8 makes no difference
9 work ethic
10 post-modern society

UNIT 24

1 pangs of hunger
2 death throes
3 cold war
4 radical fringe
5 nuclear family
6 affect the outcome
7 set very high standards
8 hot air
9 warm welcome
10 breathtaking views